Electricity From Biomass

Edited by

G Grassi, G Trebbi & D C Pike

Published by *cpl* PRESS 1992

Electricity from Biomass
Edited by: G Grassi, G Trebbi & D C Pike

ISBN 1 872691 45 5

Published by: *cpl* PRESS

CPL Press is a division of

CPL Scientific Ltd,
Science House, Winchcombe Road, Newbury,
Berkshire,RG14 5QX,
United Kingdom

Tel: +44 635 524064 Fax: +44 635 529322

Reproduced from authors' disks
Illustrations and layout by: Mrs Katy Hall
Printed by: The Chameleon Press, London

Contents

Authors & Editors

O Back is a mechanical engineer. He works in the research department of Daimler-Benz on the design of new mobile gas turbines. He is the coordinator in the CEC project: Biomass Turbine for Cogeneration (BTC).

Dr W Baldauf is an engineer employed by Veba Oel AG in Germany; he leads a group working on hydrogenation processes in a department studying alternative energies. He has studied coal liquefaction, upgrading of heavy oil residues and the upgrading of biomass-derived oils. He coordinates the working group on upgrading and characterisation of pyrolysis oils from biomass in the CEC's Joule programme.

Dr Ing A A C M Beenackers is the Professor of Chemical Engineering at Groningen University in The Netherlands. He is the author of over 120 research papers, including 50 papers on thermochemical conversion of biomass and ten papers on chemical modifications of starch. He is also a CEC expert on thermochemical conversion techniques, an adviser on energy projects for several development agencies and a consultant to some internationally operating chemical process, and process equipment, industries.

R H Booth is a chemical engineer who has worked for Shell for 30 years, including assignments in Indonesia, USA, Pakistan and the Netherlands. He is responsible for renewable energy and new business development.

Dr A V Bridgwater is Reader in Chemical Engineering at Aston University, Birmingham, UK and Chairman of the University's Energy Research Group. He is also a CEC expert, and coordinates DG XII's research programme on thermochemical conversion of biomass.

Dr J Coombs is technical director of CPL Scientific Ltd, a UK based company offering consultancy and information services to the agriculture, food, waste treatment and biomass industries. He is an expert for DG XII on biological conversion. His work on photorespiration and photosynthesis contributed to an understanding of the biochemistry of high yielding grasses such as sugar cane, sorghum and *Miscanthus* now known as C4 plants.

Professor B Delmon is Head of the Laboratory of Heterogeneous Catalysis and Chemistry of Dispersed Materials at the University of Louvain, at Louvain-la-Neuve, Belgium. He is a Member of the Belgian Academy Council of Applied Sciences. His laboratory is active in the fields of catalysis and preparation of catalysts.

T P Elliott has degrees in mechanical engineering and economics. He worked in engineering and marketing of a range of products from gas turbines to electronics before joining the Shell International Petroleum Company (SIPC) in 1980. He is actively involved in business development activities in forestry, biotechnology and renewable energy.

Dr G Gosse is Head of the INRA Bioclimatology Station at Grignon. His research group is active in the fields of crop photosynthesis and productivity modelling. The group has focused his activities on industrial and energy crops. He co-ordinates DG XII - Joule's research programme on production of biomass from agricultural crops.

Dr G Grassi is a mechanical and nuclear engineer, and has worked on technical and policy matters in Italy, UK, France and Belgium. For the past twelve years he has worked within DG XII of CEC in Brussels, and since 1988 he has led research and development activities on bio-energy, and the associated support for large European biomass energy (LEBEN) schemes.

P J Hurd is a mechanical engineer with an interest in thermodynamics. He is the Head of Development Engineering at Ruston Gas Turbines, Technology Division of European Gas Turbines. He has over 25 years' experience in gas turbine technology, and has special interests in non-standard fuels and environmental issues.

Dr E Laurent is a chemist who has been working in the laboratory of Prof Delmon for four years, and is in charge of a CEC research project on the upgrading of pyrolysis oil by hydrotreatment. This is part of a series of programmes for CEC on the use of biomass for energy or chemicals which has been proceeding for eleven years.

Dr P Mitchell is a Senior Lecturer in the Department of Forestry at the University of Aberdeen, where he leads the Wood Supply Research Group. He is a CEC expert on forestry and also advises the International Energy Agency on this subject.

Dr W Palz is the Director of research and development on renewable energies within DG XII of the CEC.

D C Pike is an engineer and geologist. He is a director of a UK company that builds and operates power stations that run on landfill gas. He acts as a consultant to the construction, waste disposal, and energy industries. He is immediate past Chairman of the UK Association of Independent Electricity Producers. He is also a CEC expert in the biomass programme.

Dr C Rossi is an electrical engineer who works in the research laboratories of ENEL, the Italian state electricity utility. He is currently studying new fuels for thermal electrical generating plants, including municipal waste and biomass.

Prof W Stander is a technology application scientist and developed the first exploitation of large freshwater springs in the sea as well as an advanced automated sub-irrigation system. Recently he has become interested in rapidly growing plants and their use. He has economic, environmentally friendly inventions in areas of use of plants for energy, housing, degradable plastics, packaging materials, etc.

Dr G Trebbi is an electrical engineer. He is head of the Pisa research laboratory at ENEL, the Italian state electricity utility, which has several research programmes on electricity from biomass.

Preface

Since the 1970s, the European Commission (CEC) has been supporting research and development into the production and use of biomass (trees, agricultural crops and wastes, etc) for energy and industrial raw materials. The work is coordinated through CEC DGXII F-4 (Head: Dr G Grassi). Recently, attention has turned to the use of biomass for the production of electricity.

To assist in the heightening of awareness among policy-makers and their advisers in both the public and private sectors it has been decided to produce this book. It does not deal with research in any great depth, but it sets out the main concepts concerning the sources of suitable biomass, their production and harvesting, their conversion into fuels, the technologies for electricity production, and the economics of the processes.

Conversion factors and Abbreviations

1 GJ_e = 277.8 kWh,   1 tce = 26.9 GJ,   1 toe = 44.8 GJ = 7.5 bbl.
GJ = giga joule = 10^9 joules. GJ_e = GJ electricity in contrast to GJ_t = GJ thermal (usually represented by GJ with no subscript except where distinction is required). kWh = kilo Watt hour. BDT = bone dry tonne (water-free weight). tce = tonne coal equivalent. toe = tone oil equivalent. bbl = barrel

ECU = European currency unit = (approx) \$US1 = £UK0.7 = Belgium F40 = Danish K8 = French F7 = German M2˙= Greek Dr200 = Irish Pt0.9 = Italy L1500 = Netherland Fl2.3 = Portuguese Esc180 = Spain Pt130.

1. Introduction

Biomass is a term used to describe materials of biological (mainly plant) origin, either purpose-grown or arising as by-products, residues or wastes from forestry, agriculture and food processing. Historically, biomass in the form of wood and farm residues and wastes was the principal source of fuel throughout the world, and so it remains in the rural areas of many developing countries. In the developed world, coal, oil and natural gas, and to a lesser extent nuclear energy, have replaced biomass.

Biomass is a regenerable energy source dependent on solar energy. Through photosynthesis, plants convert carbon dioxide into organic chemicals used in their growth. Energy can be recovered from the plant material by several processes, the simplest of which is burning in air. The carbon dioxide produced in this way makes no cumulative effect on the Greenhouse Effect, provided that the cycle of regrowth and burning is sustained.

The reasons why biomass is still used widely in developing countries are that, at the most basic level, it is often readily available, and needs little capital or technology. The converse is true in the developed world, where there is intensive land-use for high-value food crops. There, the disadvantages of biomass, compared with fossil fuels, have tipped the scales against it. Purpose grown biomass is little used in the developed world because it is diffuse and often seasonal; it has low physical and energy densities; it often has a high moisture content; and it may suffer rapid bio-degradation in storage. Growing, harvesting, transporting, storing, processing and using biomass all consume energy. The costs of these factors will discourage the use of biomass unless political initiatives are taken and incentives given.

Interest in biomass is growing partly because an awareness of economic and political factors associated with other fuels; the Gulf war has again focussed attention on the possible insecurity of the supply of oil, and Chernobyl and other accidents have undermined public confidence in nuclear energy. Furthermore, pressure for environmental protection and liberalisation of agricultural markets are combining in Europe to suggest a new rationale for energy crops grown on agricultural and marginal lands.

A considerable amount of information is already available about the selection, cultivation and harvesting of suitable plant species, and about their conversion into fuels and the use of those fuels. There are, however, gaps in knowledge which prevent the most effective use of resources. This paper reviews what is known about electricity production from biomass, and points to developments in progress or planned by the European Commission.

2. Identification of suitable crops, production and harvesting

Previous national and European research programmes have identified the most promising crops to produce energy. Two broad groups of species should be considered:

(a) Species that produce lignocellulose. Among the woody species, poplar is suitable for northern Europe, and eucalyptus is preferred for southern Europe. Among herbaceous species, *Cynara* sp. are useful for arid zones, sweet sorghum is suitable for mid- and southern Europe, and *Miscanthus* is promising for some parts of northern Europe.

(b) Species that produce fermentable carbohydrate. Sugar, starch or inulin may be produced from classical crops (wheat, sugar beet, etc) and also from such lesser-known species as Jerusalem artichoke and sweet sorghum, which offer high potential yields. Sweet sorghum produces about 30 per cent sugar and 70 per cent bagasse, a lignocellulose raw material.

2.1 Suitable herbaceous crops

2.1.1 Introduction. For electricity production from biomass, lignocellulose-producing species should be seen as the more important category. The present CEC research programme on these agricultural crops has two main aims:

(a) to improve productivity in various European conditions, from north to south, and on both high grade and marginal lands; and

(b) to achieve improved productivity without compromising the environment, in particular by reducing requirements for water and nitrogen.

2.1.2 Research activities on herbaceous crops. Activities have been focussed on those species (sweet sorghum, *Miscanthus* and *Cynara*) that present high potential productivity, and which prosper across the range of combinations of European climatic conditions and soils. The following research methodology is being applied:

(a) Potential yields are defined and expressed in relation to climatic parameters such as temperature and global radiation.

(b) The effects of stresses, such as deprivation of water and/or one or more minerals, especially nitrogen, are investigated. Activities are focused on water and nitrogen because of their important influences on production costs and environmental impacts.

(c) Quality criteria are set for the crops in the context of the provision of raw materials for different end-uses (electricity production, pulp for paper, etc).

(d) Productivity studies are complemented by genetic, physiological, economic and harvesting studies.

2.1.3 Results achieved with herbaceous crops. Table 2.1 gives the first results of productivity measurements on a herbaceous crop (sweet sorghum) for electricity production. The following points should also be noted:

(a) For sweet sorghum, the first year of experiment has confirmed the high potentiality of the existing cultivars in southern and mid-Europe. For example in Italy, more than 30 tonnes of dry matter has been produced per hectare, including 30 per cent of sugar. Moreover, this species presents a very good water efficiency. New cultivars are now being tested in northern and eastern Germany, and preliminary results are promising. The energy ratio (energy output divided by energy input) for the production of this crop, including harvesting, is about 32.

(b) There is less information about *Miscanthus* and other perennial C4 species, but it seems that some of them are relatively well adapted to northern and continental conditions. Yields of 20 to 25 tonnes of dry matter per hectare may be expected.

(c) Species adapted to dry areas, such as *Cynara cardunculus*, show very good water efficiency and are likely to be suitable for Mediterranean zones with mild winters. In these conditions, yields of 23 to 26 tonnes of dry matter may be reached.

(d) Potential yields have been estimated by different methods according to the location. In southern Europe, improvement of potential yield is not the first priority: it is better to improve the water efficiency, or to improve economic efficiency, by a good succession of crops, such as rape and sorghum. In northern Europe, potential yield may be improved by breeding adaptation to low temperature, which is the main limiting factor. This problem has been solved to some extent for maize, the range of which has gradually extended north and south.

[*Note:* The term C4 is applied to some, mainly herbaceous, plants including a number of well known grass crops such as sugar cane, maize and sorghum. These plants have an additional mechanism for trapping carbon dioxide from the atmosphere and reducing losses resulting from a light-dependent oxidation process known as photorespiration. The C4 plants generally require more sunlight and higher average temperatures to grow well since this additional mechanism requires more energy to fix the same amount of carbon than conventional temperate plants (termed C3 species). Since C4 plants do not loose any of the fixed carbon in the light they can have high productivities.]

Table 2.1. Trials of the productivity of sweet sorghum.

Location	Research body	Year	Cultivars	Yield - tonnes of dry matter per hectare per year	
				Actual	Potential
Madrid Spain	ETSIA	1990	Var Keller (with irrigation)	45 (32% sugar)	50 (35% sugar)
Bari Italy	University	1990	Var Keller (with irrigation)	46	50
Seligenstad Germany	KWS	1982 to 1985	5 cultivars	21	
Seligenstad Germany	KWS	1989	new KWS hybrid	28 (25% sugar)	30 (35% sugar)
Forli Italy	A Biotec	1986	Var Keller	24 (26 to 33% sugar)	30 (35% sugar)
Lusignan France	INRA	1990	Var Keller (with irrigation)	24 (31% sugar)	30 (35% sugar)
			Var Keller (under dry conditions)	14 (33% sugar)	
Grignon France	INRA	1989 1990	Var Keller	21 18 (31% sugar)	30 (35% sugar)
Cork Ireland	HYPERION	1990	Var Keller	<6	Unlikely to be interesting
Noircourt Belgium	SORGHAL	1990	Var Korall	33	30 (35% sugar)
Essex UK	University	1990	Var Keller	5	Unlikely to be interesting

2.2 Short rotation forestry

Short rotation forestry using coppicing species has great potential within the European Community. Species being considered include willows in the north west, poplars in northern and middle Europe, *Robinia* in the Mediterranean region and *Eucalyptus* in the Iberian peninsular and parts of France. These crops are suitable for growth on land set aside from agricultural production.

Research has been conducted into production systems for these crops for the last ten years or so. Special harvesters need to be designed as the crops are unusual and existing equipment is inappropriate. Harvesting costs are significant and can amount to 50 to 70 per cent of the final cost of delivery to the user.

The economics of energy coppices in the UK have been examined with simple mathematical models, which can also be applied elsewhere in the EC, given the necessary inputs.

These models have been used to examine systems based on 3-year and 5-year cutting cycles. A harvesting cost of 27 ECU per dry tonne has been assumed, based on trials with the Loughry Coppice Harvester. Two scenarios have been modelled: in the first, a farmer grows the crop using opportunity labour, and hires contractors to harvest the crop. In the second, contractors are used for all operations. The unit costs of operations are important inputs to the modelling of economics. Assumed values for costs (Nix, 1990) are shown in Table 2.2.

For energy coppice to be made attractive to farmers, it has to be shown to provide at least as good a return as other competing agricultural crops, using language that farmers understand. The usual way to express the financial performance of agricultural enterprises is in terms of gross margins (GM), but this concept is applicable only to annual crops.

When dealing with crops taken over longer time periods (e.g. forest products), the equivalent annual value (EAV) can be used as a proxy for gross margin (Insley, Harper and Whiteman, 1987). Agricultural economists discount the costs of using labour and machinery already hired directly or possessed by a farmer; these are visualised as being lower than the cost of hiring a contractor.

In valuing the product, it is assumed that wood could be sold for fuel at 3.4 ECU per GJ (for wood having an energy content of 18 GJ per oven-dry tonne). This is equivalent to 143 ECU per tonne oil equivalent and to 61 ECU per dry tonne wood [ed.]. Table 2.3 shows results of three analyses to test the sensitivity of the potential market to energy prices and productivity.

Table 2.2. Costs of operations in energy coppicing

Operation	Year in which the operation is carried out	Cost of each operation - ECU per hectare	
		Farmer system	Contractor system
5 year cutting cycle			
Site preparation	0	86	140
Planting	0	1437	1677
Herbicide 1	0	7	7
Herbicide 2	1, 6, 11, 16	86	126
Cut-back[2]	0	0	286
Gapping-up[3]	0	0	57
Fertilise	6, 11, 16	20	40
Harvest	5, 10, 15, 20	1606	1606
3 year cutting cycle			
Site preparation	0	86	140
Planting	0	2145	2488
Herbicide 1	0	7	27
Herbicide 2	1, 4, 7, 10, 13, 16, 19	86	140
Cut-back[2]	0	0	286
Gapping-up[3]	0	0	57
Fertilise	4, 7, 10, 13, 16, 19	20	40
Harvest	3, 6, 9, 12, 15, 18, 21	964	964

Notes:

1. These costs apply to systems producing 12 dry tonnes per hectare per year in the long term.

2. The young trees are cut back to stimulate growth.

3. If some of the original plantings are dead, they are replaced with cuttings from the cut-back process.

Agricultural economics are dominated by grants and subsidies. A new system of grant aid for short rotation forestry has recently been made available in the UK. This will be payable from April 1992, and will markedly improve the economics.

On better land such payments will reduce attributed production costs for a system operated by the farmer himself and producing 12 dry tonnes per hectare per year, to 14 and 8 ECU per dry tonne for the 3- and 5-year cycles, respectively. Under a system with a similar output but operated by a contractor, the costs would be reduced to 24 and 17 ECU per dry tonne, respectively.

Thus, under the new grant system for energy coppice in the UK, the farmer could achieve an EAV of 448 ECU per hectare. This compares with annual values of GM for enterprises producing winter wheat and lowland beef of about 680 and 386 ECU per hectare, respectively. In considering these figures, it should be remembered that all agricultural subsidies in the EC are under review, and that there is world-wide pressure to reduce subsidies on food crops.

Table 2.3 Economic modelling of energy coppice.

Cycle -	Yield -	Farmer		Contractor	
years	dry tonnes per hectare per year	Cost ECU per dry tonne	EAV ECU per hectare	Cost ECU per dry tonne	EAV ECU per hectare
5	12	32	216	37	152
5	16	30	283	35	226
3	12	37	176	44	93

3. Conversion into fuels

3.1 Gasification

3.1.1 Introduction. Gasification is a technology for the thermochemical conversion of organic material into useful gases. For example, biomass or coal can be reacted with oxygen to produce mainly carbon monoxide and hydrogen, which can be used as a fuel or a chemical feedstock.

In principle, the technology is not much different from combustion, in which organic material also reacts with oxygen, though in the latter case the main products are carbon dioxide and water. Whether a process results in gasification or combustion depends on the air to fuel ratio applied. If biomass is assumed to have the composition of cellulose, $C_6H_{10}O_5$, gasification and combustion can be represented as chemical reactions as follows:

$$C_6H_{10}O_5 + 0.5\ O_2 \rightarrow 6\ CO + 5\ H_2 \quad \text{- gasification}$$

$$C_6H_{10}O_5 + 6\ O_2 \rightarrow 6\ CO_2 + 5\ H_2O \quad \text{- combustion}$$

In the combustion reaction, much more heat is given off (17.5 MJ/kg) than in the gasification reaction (1.85 MJ/kg). Thus, whereas combustion converts the chemical energy of a feedstock into heat, gasification is a technology to convert a solid carrier of chemical energy into a gaseous carrier. The gas obtained in gasification still can be combusted in a second step, resulting in the liberation of the chemical energy of the gas in the form of heat, by the following reactions:

$$CO + 0.5\ O_2 \rightarrow CO_2$$

$$H_2 + 0.5\ O_2 \rightarrow H_2O$$

With respect to electricity generation from biomass, the question is: why is it appropriate to apply gasification followed by combustion instead of direct combustion of the biomass? One reason is related to the significantly better burning properties of a gas relative to a solid: i.e. process control is easier, hardly any excess of air is necessary, simple burners can be used, and there are no particulate emissions and less gaseous pollutants.

A second reason is that the gas obtained from gasification can be directly converted to shaft power by combustion in a gas turbine, gas or dual-fuel diesel engine. This avoids the less efficient, indirect steam cycle, which is generally used with the combustion of solids to transfer the heat from the combustion gases via a steam turbine into shaft power to drive the electricity generator.

8

Therefore, electricity plants based on gasification have higher overall efficiencies than those based on combustion, particularly at the relatively low capacities relevant in biomass conversion technology (typically below 100 MW_e). In these circumstances, even taking into account the capital and running costs of gasification plant, the economics of electricity production of biomass via gasification are believed to be more favourable than those of systems using direct combustion.

Gasification is a classical technology that has been known for more than 250 years (Hales, 1727), and during the second world war the technology reached full maturity in Germany, so that nearly all modern gasifiers are based on ideas already commercialized in the early '40s. After the war, gasification technology faded away nearly everywhere because of the world-wide availability of cheap crude oil. The exception is South Africa, where large coal gasification plants make that country relatively self-sufficient in its energy needs. Recently, coal gasification for electricity production has reached the commercial scale with capacities of several hundred megawatts. Such a plant of 250 MW_e capacity is now under construction at Buggenum, in The Netherlands.

There was renewed interest in the gasification of biomass as a result of the energy crisis of the 1970s, and since then the Commission of the European Communities has supported several programmes on developing advanced gasification technology. As a result of this research, technology for small scale gasification (up to 1 MW_e) has reached the commercial scale, and larger scale biomass gasification technology for electricity has reached a degree of development that justifies a demonstration plant in the range of 20 to 100 MW_e.

3.1.2 *Downdraft moving bed gasifiers.* Downdraft moving bed gasification, using air as the gasifying agent, is the most widely applied technology on a small scale below 1 MW. A scheme of such a gasifier for wood and wood wastes is shown in Figure 3.1. The system is not very much different from a domestic stove, except that gasifiers must have excellent insulation. The poorer the insulation, the more the reactor behaves like a stove, and the more CO_2 and H_2O are produced at the expense of reduced outputs of CO and H_2. The gasifier operates as follows:

(a) Biomass is fed continuously through a bin at the top in such a way that the bed level in the gasifier remains within certain limits. Producer gas is continuously sucked off at the bottom below a grate, usually by the engine that is fuelled by this gas. Continuous removal of producer gas causes air to be continuously sucked into the bed. Figure 3.1 shows a central air inlet, but multiple side inlets, just above the throat, are common.

9

(b) Around the air entrances rapid, exothermic, partial combustion occurs at temperatures above 1,000°C, causing char to be deposited in a bed below the air inlet, according to the following reaction:

$$2(C_6H_{10}O_5) + O_2 \rightarrow 11 \, C + CO_2 + 10 \, H_2O$$

(c) In the zone below the air inlet, gasification takes place according to the following endothermic reactions:

$$C + CO_2 \rightarrow 2 \, CO$$

$$C + H_2O \rightarrow CO + H_2$$

If wood is the feedstock, the heat produced in the combustion zone is used to dry it in the zone above the air inlet and to drive the endothermic gasification reactions. The wetter the wood and the greater the heat loss, the less heat remains for the gasification reactions, and hence the lower the heating value of the gas produced. Ideally the moisture content of the wood should always be below 25 per cent.

Above the air inlet, wood starts to pyrolyse. Throat gas circulation patterns are induced above the throat, causing an intense mixing of the pyrolysis gas with the hot gas in the oxidation zone. By this means, all pyrolysis gases are oxidized, so that the resulting gas is very low in tars. Although ingenious scale-up methods have been proposed (Groeneveld, 1983), this technology in practice has found application for power generation only at a scale of a few megawatts, or less. Such small capacities are economically feasible only in developing countries, and it is there that these reactors are found in significant numbers. Most designs accept regular wood blocks only, but a dedicated design has been developed for rice husks (Manurung and Beenackers, 1985 and 1989).

3.1.3 *Circulating fluidized bed gasifiers.* In the developed world, electricity from biomass plants typically will have capacities in the range of 10 to 100 MW_e. For such capacities, conventional fluidized beds, and (especially) circulating fluidized beds, are the most attractive options. Extensive research over the past decade within the European Community has allowed at least three European manufacturers to be able to offer this technology now. The principle of circulating fluid bed is shown in Figure 3.2. Small particles of biomass (typically a few mm in diameter) are continuously fed to the gasifier by a screw feeder. Air or oxygen is fed as the gasifying agent at the bottom. Gas velocities in circulating beds are so high that a significant fraction of the inert solids is entrained over the top of the bed. These solids are recirculated to the bed via a cyclone separator.

In a normal fluidized bed, reactor gas velocities are lower (about 0.5m per second); as a result, the carry-over of solids is relatively small. Often a secondary gasifying agent is fed on top of the bed to obtain a tar-free gas. The bed temperature (typically 820°C) and the gas composition are highly influenced by the oxygen:fuel ratio, and the moisture content of the fuel. Typical data for air gasification based on wood having a moisture content of 20 per cent are as follows (Chavot, 1990):

Air feed: 1.8 Nm^3/kg dry wood
Producer gas yield: 2.5 Nm^3/kg dry wood
Lower Heating Value of dry gas: 4,400 kJ/Nm^3

To give the best economic results, fluidized beds are operated under pressure, typically between 10 and 30 bar. Conventional fluidized bed wood gasifiers have already operated under such pressures e.g. at the Clamecy and Espoo units (Stein industries, unpublished; Kurkela *et al*, 1989).

3.1.4 *Advanced gasification.* Research, partly funded by the CEC, has been carried out on more advanced processes, for example on oxygen and steam gasification of biomass (Beenackers and Van Swaaij, 1986).

3.2 Biomass pyrolysis liquids production

3.2.1 *Introduction.* Pyrolysis is a technology for the conversion of biomass into gas, liquid and char - the relative proportions depending very much on the pyrolysis method and reaction parameters. Fast or flash pyrolysis is used to maximise either gas or liquid products according to the temperature employed.

Pyrolysis is thermal degradation, either in the complete absence of oxidising agent, or with such a limited supply that gasification does not occur to an appreciable extent. Heat is usually added indirectly, in a variety of forms, although partial gasification may be employed to give direct heating. Relatively low temperatures are employed: 400 to 800°C. The modes of pyrolysis are summarised below with key process parameters:

(a) Slow pyrolysis at low temperatures and long reaction times maximises charcoal yields at about 30 per cent by weight, comprising about 50 per cent of the energy content of the feedstock.

(b) Flash pyrolysis at relatively low temperatures (typically 500°C, but not more than 750°C) and at very high reaction rates and short residence times of typically less than 1 second, maximises liquid yields at up to 80 per cent by weight.

11

(c) Flash pyrolysis similar to (b), but at relatively high temperatures (above 700°C) maximises gas yields at up to 80 per cent by weight.

(d) Conventional pyrolysis at moderate temperatures of less than about 600°C and moderate reaction rates gives approximately equal proportions of gas, liquid and solid products.

A typical pyrolysis process is illustrated in Figure 3.3 (based on the Ensyn RTP III process). Prepared dried biomass is fed into a transport reactor and contacted with hot, recirculated sand. The products are passed through two cyclones to separate first sand and then char. Next, the liquid is rapidly quenched and cooled. The total residence time for the hot vapours can be controlled down to a few hundred milliseconds which retains the thermally unstable, liquid intermediates of pyrolysis. Most flash pyrolysis processes employ similar concepts to minimise vapour residence time.

A review of the major biomass pyrolysis activities has been published which contains descriptions and flowsheets of 13 pyrolysis processes (Bridgwater and Bridge, 1991).

Of particular interest is the direct production of liquids, because their much higher energy density reduces transport and handling costs, and because they are easy to substitute for conventional fuels in many static applications such as boilers and for process heat (Bridgwater and Bridge, 1991).

The options for pyrolysis processing, with their products and applications, are summarised in Figure 3.4. Secondary processes, giving a range of higher value products, are also illustrated.

3.2.2 *Liquid products.* The liquid product of pyrolysis is a very complex mixture of oxygenated hydrocarbons, the composition of which is determined intrinsically by the rate of reaction and product quenching, and extrinsically by the feed composition. The complexity arises from the relatively uncontrolled degradation of lignin, producing a broad spectrum of phenolic and similar types of compounds that inter-react (Evans and Milne, 1987). The liquid is referred to as "oil", "bio-oil" or "bio-crude-oil". It can be upgraded to liquid hydrocarbon fuels. There are two types of liquids produced by pyrolysis of biomass:

(a) Primary bio-oil from flash pyrolysis processes.

(b) Secondary oil or tar from conventional or slow pyrolysis processes, as well as by-products from gasification.

Table 3.1. Wood-derived pyrolysis oils from Ensyn, Canada (Information supplied by Ensyn Engineering Ltd.)

Physical property	Typical value	Probable range
Moisture content - per cent	16	12 to 20
pH	2.5	2.1 to 3.3
Specific gravity	1.21	1.11 to 1.25
Elemental analysis (moisture free) - per cent by weight		
C	56.4	51 to 58
H	6.2	5.1 to 7.1
N	0	0.16 to 0.35
S	0.1	0 to 0.03
Ash	0.1	0.03 to 0.3
Higher Heating Value - MJ/kg		
moisture free basis	23	22.1 to 24.3
as produced	19.3	
Viscosity at 40°C - cp	51	40 to 59
Kinematic Viscosity - cSt - at:		
25°C	233	
40°C	134	
ASIM Vacuum Distillation - % - at:		
160°C	10	
193°C	20	
219°C	40	
Distillate	50	
Pour point	23°C	
Solubility - per cent		
hexane insoluble	99	
toluene insoluble	84	
acetone/acetic acid insoluble	0.14	

Table 3.2. Comparison of characteristics of liquids - typical data (Information supplied by Ensyn Engineering Ltd or taken from Antonelli, 1988 [Alten data]).

	Ensyn Flash pyrolysis	Alten Slow pyrolysis
Moisture content - per cent	16	14.6
pH	2.5	2.0
Specific gravity	1.21	1.195
Elemental analysis (moisture free) - per cent		
C	56.4	61.9
H	6.2	6.0
N	0.2	1.05
S	<0.01	0.03
Ash	0.1	1.5
O (by difference)	37.1	29.5
C/H ratio	9.1	10.3
Higher Heating Value MJ/kg		
moisture-free basis	23	26.3
as produced	19.3	
Viscosity at 40°C - cp	51	300
Pour Point - °C	-23	-27

These differ in several important aspects that affect their storage, handling and utilisation. Almost all attention is now focussed on flash pyrolysis liquids because of their much higher yields and superior properties. Table 3.1 lists typical and ranges of values for many important properties of flash pyrolysis oil from the Ensyn process (Graham, private communication), while Table 3.2 compares this data with that from a conventional (slow) pyrolysis process.

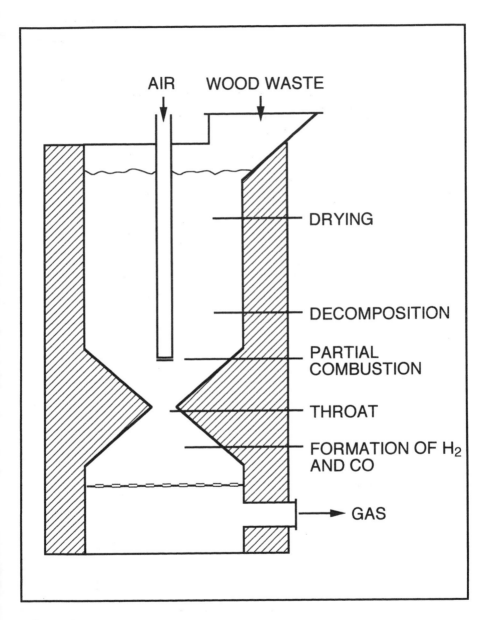

Figure 3.1. Co-current, moving bed gasifier with central air inlet (after Groenveld, 1983).

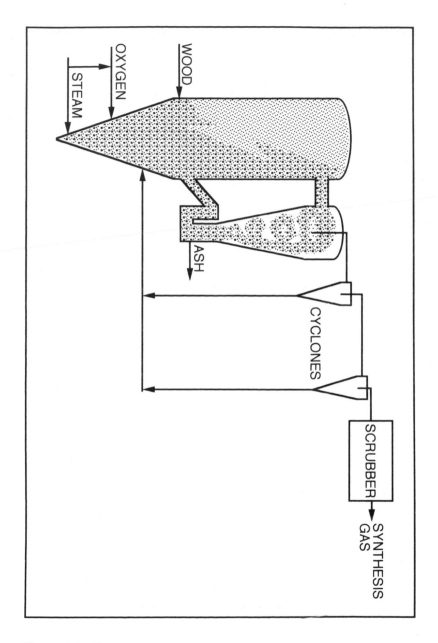

Figure 3.2. Circulating fluidized bed gasifier (*Lurgi*).

3.2.3 *Thermal stability.* Deterioration of liquid product can be caused by temperatures above about 100°C, which adversely affect properties such as: viscosity; phase separation; and deposition of a bitumen-like substance resulting from polymerization and other reactions resulting from the high oxygen content of bio-oil. Proposals to heat the liquid to reduce its viscosity, e.g. for pumping or atomisation, need to be considered carefully and thoroughly tested to avoid exposing the liquid to any temperature above 100°C. In-line steam heating to 90°C appears to be a successful approach. Exposure to air also causes deterioration, but at a slower rate than temperature increase. Maintenance of the liquid in a sealed enclosure obviously minimises exposure to oxygen, but could cause a substantial pressure increase if temperatures increase, so some minimal venting is necessary. Pyrolysis liquid is reported as having been stored in this way in a usable form for up to two years without problems. Its low pH arises from the content of organic acids (e.g. acetic and formic acids), and it is therefore corrosive. Thus, mild steel is unsuitable for pipes, storage vessels or other equipment to be in contact with the liquid; polypropylene has been used successfully to overcome this problem.

3.2.4 *Particulates.* Particulate levels may be high as a result of carry-over of char and ash from the reactor. Separation of solids is usually carried out by a primary cyclone downstream of the reactor to minimise reaction time and is not very effective for small particles of char. Secondary separation of char from condensed liquid is poorly understood and little research has been carried out. Utilisation of crude liquid with char in suspension has to be tolerated until separation techniques have been developed.

3.2.5 *Water.* The water content of the bio-oil is important as it:

(a) reduces the heating value,

(b) affects the pH,

(c) reduces the viscosity,

(d) influences both chemical and physical stability, and

(e) reduces potential pollution problems by eliminating waste water.

The water content can also affect subsequent upgrading processes. Water is difficult to remove from bio-oil, as evaporation or distillation at normal temperatures of around 100°C causes significant, and potentially deleterious, physical and chemical changes in the liquid as described above. Pyrolysis liquids should, therefore, be utilised without water removal whenever possible.

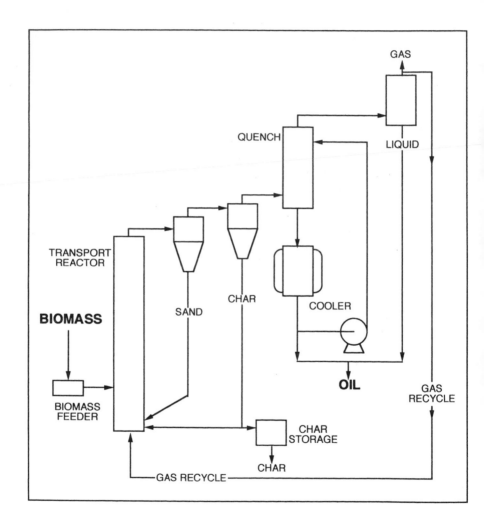

Figure 3.3. Ensyn RTP pyrolysis process flowsheet.

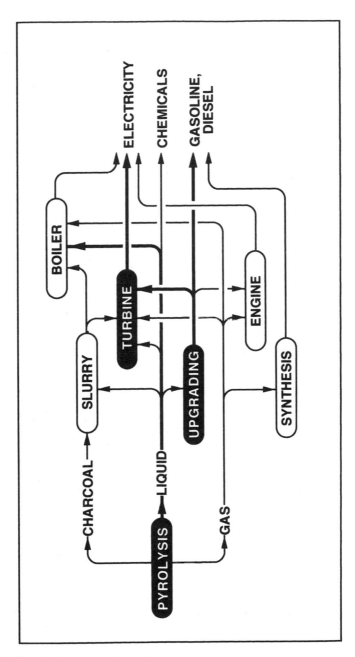

Figure 3.4. Pyrolysis conversion pathways.

3.2.6 Compatibility. Pyrolysis liquids are immiscible with conventional fuels and should not be expected to be assimilated within a conventional fuel marketing infrastructure without some conversion or upgrading. Theoretically, it would be possible to create a discrete system for the storage, distribution and utilisation of pyrolysis liquids, managed by experts who understand the special problems and advantages of this fuel, but this would be viable only in exceptional conditions.

An acceptable and feasible alternative is to dedicate the whole output of the product, without much further processing, to a specific application such as a thermal power station that will accept lower quality oils.

3.2.7 Comparison of primary and secondary liquids. Water separation is one of the major differences between the products of flash pyrolysis (primary liquids) and the products of slow pyrolysis (secondary liquids). Primary liquids can absorb up to 50 per cent by weight of water, or more, before separation occurs, whereas secondary liquids have a maximum water loading of about 20 per cent, depending on the technology employed.

Water separation from liquids from slow pyrolysis processes is thus likely, leading to a potentially significant waste-water disposal problem that does not occur with flash pyrolysis products. Because viscosity, and hence pour point, are much lower for primary oils, they are easier to handle. Toxicity tests have suggested that primary liquids are significantly less hazardous than secondary liquids because of the lower temperature of formation.

3.2.8 Applications. Products that can be derived from pyrolysis are shown in Figure 3.4, with emphasis on the production and utilisation of liquid fuels such as bio-oil and its derivatives. Gaseous fuels are produced as a by-product and will tend to be used in the production plant for power generation, or drying feedstock. Relatively small yields of charcoal are produced, which could also be utilised for feed drying, or be sold as a fuel, possibly for slurrying to give a liquid fuel.

3.2.9 Combustion. Liquid products from the processing of biomass are easier to transport, handle and store than solids or gases. This is important when considering marketing fuel to existing combustion plant, such as steam-raising boilers. To retrofit existing equipment, only relatively minor modifications of the equipment are likely to be needed, and perhaps no changes at all in some cases. The crude liquid product may be readily burned and has been tested in this application in both Europe and North America (D. Huffman; personal communication); B. Groux; personal communication; International Flame Research Foundation, 1990). Few problems have been reported in its use, although special precautions may have to be taken with equipment used in handling, storage and combustion, such as atomisers. One aspect not yet resolved is that of emissions, and tests are currently in progress.

3.2.10 *Electricity generation.* As noted elsewhere in this publication, there are advantages in using gas turbines, fuelled with products from biomass, for the generation of electricity. In principle, gas turbines can be fired with pyrolytic oils, but there is hardly any practical experience to date, although work is in progress (Grassi and Bridgwater, 1990). Table 3.2 above shows one of the potential problems in the high carbon:hydrogen ratios, which may cause combustion problems. Substantial re-design may be necessary to accommodate the different flame characteristics and maintain low emissions of pollutants such as NO_x.

One possibility is to re-design the turbine burner, another is to upgrade the liquid to a more compatible composition by reducing the carbon:hydrogen ratio. Most work on upgrading by hydrotreating has concentrated on total oxygen removal to produce hydrocarbon fuels compatible with conventional fossil derived fuels. However, it may be more cost- and energy-effective to carry out partial upgrading to give a fuel that gives acceptable results in a gas turbine, but without going to the extent of meeting a specification for a conventional fuel. This has not yet been studied, but it offers the prospect of a more stable liquid that is less susceptible to temperature variations and oxygen absorption.

3.2.11 *Current status of pyrolysis processes.* There has been a significant level of activity in North America for over ten years with a number of processes being developed to demonstration and commercial operation including the 1,360 kg/h demonstration plant built by Interchem in Missouri, USA, and the commercial operations of Ensyn in Canada, where a 1,000 kg/h plant is being built. A number of new projects have recently started in the current Energy from Biomass programme in the EEC JOULE programme, including a 200 kg/h entrained flow pilot plant in Belgium and several smaller research units. In addition, a 250 kg/h pilot plant based on the Canadian Waterloo process is being constructed by Union Electrica Fenosa in Spain with a planned start-up in 1991, and other pilot-scale flash pyrolysis plants are being planned by the state electricity company ENEL in Italy and by the Centre for Renewable Energy Sources in Greece.

A number of demonstration plants for flash pyrolysis are operating in North America at a scale of up to 50 kg/h with plans for several commercial developments ranging up to 40 t/h in the USA, Canada, Europe and Australia. Examples of current research and development activities are listed in Table 3.3.

Table 3.3. Current and recent research and development activities.

Organisation	Technology	Country	Capacity kg/h	Status
Interchem	Ablative	USA	1360	Shake-down
Ensyn Engineering	Transport	Canada	1000	Construction
KTI + Italenergie	Conventional	Italy	500	Dormant
Ensyn Engineering	Transport	Canada	300	Operational
Union Electrica Fenosa/Waterloo Univ	Flash fluid bed	Spain/Canada	250	Construction
Egemin	Entrained flow	Belgium	250	Construction
Georgia Technical Research Institute	Entrained flow	USA	50	Dormant
Laval University	Vacuum	Canada	50	Operational
Solar Energy Research Institute	Ablative	USA	50	Operational
Wastewater Treatment Centre	Moving bed	Canada	42	Operational
CRES	Circulating bed	Greece	20	Construction
Tubingen University	Low temperature	Germany	10	Operational
Twente University	Ablative	Netherlands	10	Operational
LNETI	Fluid bed	Portugal	10	Shake-down
Waterloo University	Flash fluid bed	Canada	3	Operational
Aston University	Ablative	UK	3	Construction
CPERI	Fluid bed	Greece	< 1	Operational
Toronto University	Hydropyrolysis	Canada	batch	Dormant
ECC	Ablative	Canada	unknown	Operational

3.3 Upgrading of pyrolysis oils

Oils produced by the pyrolysis of biomass are attractive in environmental terms when compared to fuels derived from petroleum, especially because their combustion does not increase the carbon dioxide content of the atmosphere, and because of their low sulfur content. However, the crude oil products of pyrolysis from biomass have several limitations. They have a high oxygen content (around 30 per cent by mass), and they are unstable: solidification occurs when they are heated to 100 to 200°C, so they cannot be fractionated by distillation. They are not completely volatile and are poorly miscible with hydrocarbon solvents. They contain dissolved water (up to 30 per cent by mass). They are relatively viscous, and often are acidic, thus presenting corrosion problems.

The direct combustion of pyrolysis oils in gas turbines is a major objective of the CEC's research programme. There may be ways of using the crude oil, but it seems likely that at least a measure of upgrading will be necessary to ensure that the fuel can be handled and combusted efficiently without damage to the plant, and that limits on emissions are satisfactorily met. Three methods can be regarded as promising for upgrading pyrolysis oils:

(a) low pressure upgrading using zeolites;

(b) high pressure hydropurification;

(c) blending with petroleum feedstocks at oil refineries.

3.3.1 *Low pressure treatment using zeolites.* This upgrading process is based on the ability of a zeolite (ZSM-5) to convert small oxygenated organic molecules into hydrocarbons, by a process similar to one invented by Mobil for the conversion of methanol to gasoline. The products are in the gasoline range, and are obtained by dehydration and decarboxylation reactions.

This treatment has been successfully tested at the laboratory scale by several research groups for the upgrading of pyrolysis oils (Renaud, Grandmaison, Roy and Kaliaguine, 1987; Diebold and Scahill, 1987; Chang, Lang and Silvestri, 1976; Chen, Walsh and Koening, 1987; Diebold and Power, 1988). Nevertheless, some limiting aspects have to be mentioned:

(a) Because of the instability of pyrolysis oils, the treatment is preferably accomplished before any condensation of the vapours takes place at the exit of the pyrolyzer.

(b) Oxygen is eliminated from the crude oil partly as carbon monoxide and dioxide, but mainly as water. No hydrogen is added, so hydrogen is thus consumed from the oil by the production of water. The crude oil is already poor in hydrogen, so the product has a rather low yield of gasoline type product (10 to 25 per cent).

(c) Deactivation of the catalyst by coking is quite rapid, so sophisticated reactors are needed to achieve continuous catalyst regeneration.

Future research should concentrate on finding the most effective zeolite structures or modified zeolites, and on accumulating reliable data on catalyst deactivation. A better fundamental understanding of the chemical reactions is also desirable.

3.3.2 *High pressure hydropurification.* Upgrading effected in the presence of a reducing gas (hydrogen) aims at removing oxygen as water and at reducing the molecular weight of the heavy fraction of the pyrolysis oil. This process, called hydroprocessing, offers simple control of the conditions and severity of the reactions, and has a wide range of applications. It is commonly used in petroleum refining for diverse purposes like desulfurisation, denitrification, hydrogenation or hydrocracking.

Several studies have been accomplished on hydrotreatment of pyrolysis oils; these looked at the effects of changing the catalyst, the source of bio-oils and the process conditions (Elliott and Baker, 1987; Churin, Grange and Delmon; Gebert, 1987; Soltes, Lin and Sheu, 1987). The results show that hydrotreatment constitutes a promising way to improve the quality of the biomass-derived oils, although their peculiarities require careful control of the reaction conditions.

To avoid high thermal polymerization (degradation by coking) of the oil, a pre-hydrotreatment at moderate temperature (200°C) and/or co-processing with a hydrogen-donor solvent is generally needed. Conventional hydrodesulfurisation or hydrodenitrogenation catalysts (cobalt/molybdenum and nickel/molybdenum catalysts supported on alumina in the sulfided form) are preferred.

Pyrolysis oils, because of their high oxygen content, require a long reaction time for complete deoxygenation. The products obtained are in the gasoline and diesel boiling range.

Full hydrotreatment is used for the production of high grade hydrocarbon product, but partial hydrotreatment could be used for the stabilisation of the pyrolysis oils.

The severity of the process can be controlled so as to provide a given percentage of deoxygenation of the crude oils. A moderate deoxygenation might permit sufficient stabilisation of the oils so that they could be fed to, and combusted in, a gas turbine.

On the basis of current knowledge, the priorities for research are to determine the mass balance of the reaction, and the performance of catalysts under static conditions in a laboratory-scale flow reactor. The long term stability of the catalyst needs to be demonstrated. Also, the potentialities of hydrotreatment as a stabilisation method of pyrolysis oils must be assessed. Characteristics of moderately hydrotreated oils must be determined and their potentialities as fuel for gas turbine evaluated.

3.3.3 *Refining pyrolysis oils by blending into petroleum refineries.*

In standard petroleum refineries, oil processing begins with atmospheric and vacuum distillation of crude oils to obtain naphtha, kerosene, diesel, gas oil, vacuum gas oil and residue. These cuts are used directly or after blending as marketable products, or they are further upgraded. The following processes are used (feedstocks are given in brackcts):

(a) Refining, reforming (naphtha).

(b) Desulfurisation (kerosene, diesel).

(c) Coking (gas oil, vacuum gas oil, residue).

(d) Cat cracking (gas oil, vacuum gas oil).

(e) Visbreaking (gas oil, vacuum gas oil, residue).

(f) Hydrocracking (gas oil, vacuum gas oil).

(g) Residue upgrading.

It is attractive to consider blending a proportion of pyrolysis oil with petroleum-based feedstocks to the above processes, the choice depending on the boiling range of the pyrolysis oil or its fractions. Unfortunately, raw pyrolysis oils cannot be mixed with petroleum crudes or petroleum fractions. Also, heating of these oils leads to cracking and/or polymerization far below the operating temperatures of any of the above-mentioned processes. Therefore, a hydrogenating pretreatment of pyrolysis oil is necessary before it can be used in this way.

Future research should be directed at:

(a) Finding economic ways of stabilising pyrolysis oils to make them suitable for mixing with conventional petroleum cuts, and for withstanding refinery process conditions.

(b) Investigating the influence of pyrolysis oil as a blend component on the different refinery processes, with respect to yields, chemical structures, product qualities and operating behaviour (e.g. deactivation of catalysts, and blockage or corrosion of reactors).

3.4 Other processes for the conversion of biomass into fuels for production of electricity

Many vegetable-oil crops have been considered as sources for substitutes for diesel oil, and a process is now being developed for the conversion of rapeseed oil for this purpose (Chemistry and Industry, 1990). This, and the processes of gasification, pyrolysis and associated upgrading of biomass described in the earlier sections of this chapter are thermo-chemical. An alternative approach is to use bio-chemical conversion, which offers several pathways from biomass to fuel suitable for electricity generation. Two such pathways, i.e. fermentation to produce alcohol, and anaerobic digestion to produce methane, are well established in processes for other applications throughout the world and, indeed, are sometimes linked to electricity production. Other possibilities, notably hydrolysis, are under development.

Fermentation of biomass for the production of alcohol for vehicle fuel is an important industry in Brazil, Zimbabwe and the US. In 1989, Brazil produced over 9 million tonnes of fuel alcohol from sugar cane, and the US produced about 2 million tonnes from maize. These programmes require considerable government support when, as at present, the price of oil products is low.

Anaerobic digestion (AD) is often an important phase of sewage treatment in the developed world, and sewage gas (impure methane) is often used for electricity production. AD is now being applied increasingly to process wastes from farms and food factories. In developing countries, especially India and China, many small digesters exist, and the biogas from them is used commonly for heating, and sometimes for power generation. Large amounts of impure methane also arise from the uncontrolled biological decay of domestic and commercial wastes that are landfilled. Landfill gas is being utilised on a growing scale, and electricity production is an increasingly popular method for exploiting the energy in that gas which would otherwise be wasted. It also provides a safe way of reducing the danger of explosions and pollution by landfill gas.

26

4. Electricity production

4.1 Direct combustion and steam-raising

Biomass is already being used, without preliminary conversion, as a fuel for direct combustion to raise steam and hence to generate electricity. Wood, agricultural and forestry wastes, and domestic and commercial wastes can be cited as examples of fuels used in this way.

Direct combustion is well suited to the use of biomass having fairly low contents of moisture and ash. The design of the grate and boiler determines the completeness of combustion and efficiency of heat transfer. Improved designs aim to improve efficiency and to decrease noxious emissions. Other improvements include methods for using waste heat to partially dry the feedstock. Devices are available to handle most types of biomass.

In the US, many power plants are fuelled by forestry and agricultural wastes, providing about 4 GW of capacity (Elliott and Booth, 1991). Many factories that process sugar cane generate power from the associated waste bagasse; the worldwide generation capacity is about 1 GW.

Capital costs per MW of net electricity output of existing plant vary widely, because of differences in circumstances and operating requirements. If the fuel is cheap and readily available all year round, then a low-cost plant of low to medium thermal efficiency may be acceptable. But some plants have to be capable of running on fossil fuel for part of the year.

In some cases, the use of steam or waste heat in part of a process within a factory may influence the selected design. Also, if the fuel is more valuable and/or the supply is limited (for example bagasse can be used in board and paper products), steam-raising at higher pressures may be attractive, but this increases capital costs.

Commercial, industrial and domestic wastes are incinerated in special plants, with or without preliminary sorting. Full sorting permits the production of a medium-grade pelletised fuel that can be fed to ordinary coal-firing boilers.

Unrefined bio-oil produced from biomass by pyrolysis can be substituted for fuel oil in boilers, and bio-char could be mixed with bio-oil and/or water.

4.2 The gas turbine and its advantages

Following the development of the gas turbine engine for aircraft propulsion during the 1939-45 war, manufacturers in Europe and the USA embarked on designs of industrial gas turbines. Earliest designs had been based on steam turbines, having heavy cast turbine casings and solid forged rotors. These were costly and inflexible.

The trend of design was therefore to low weight and rapid manoeuvrability through the load range. To achieve this, hot gas paths were separated from structural pressure casings by the now common double-skin construction, using an internal skin of light section, heat-resisting material. Blade rings were made in several segments having radial and circumferential freedom of expansion, and rotors were assemblies of discs giving minimum mass and cooling of bores and faces, and allowing for differential expansions. This form of construction immediately yielded success. Over the succeeding 40 years, steady improvements have been made in performance, with more applications and larger units, at the same time retaining the essential simplicity and reliability of the original concept.

The industrial gas turbine has found many uses throughout the world, particularly in the oil and gas industries for pumping, compression and re-injection duties, and also for electricity generation. Commercial machines exist at sizes between tens of kW and hundreds of MW. In contrast to aero-derivatives, industrial versions of the gas turbine are purpose-designed for specific applications.

The main advantages of the gas turbine over other types of engine is their compact size, their low capital cost and their high reliability, leading to infrequent servicing and low maintenance costs. The thermal efficiency of some machines, especially in the smaller size ratings, has been low in the past because, in the era of cheap fuel, high efficiency was often not a priority for designers. However, it is now common to achieve efficiencies of 30 per cent or more. This can be raised to around 45 per cent by recovering waste heat from exhaust gases, raising steam and using that to run a steam turbine in the so-called combined cycle. In the 150 to 200 MW engine range, combined cycle efficiencies are possible with multi-pressure steam cycles.

The thermal efficiency and specific power of a gas turbine are determined by the pressure ratio and the turbine entry temperature. Specific power is strongly dependent on temperature: an increase in temperature of 100°C typically increases power by 20 per cent. Thermal efficiency considerations require that pressure ratio increases as temperature is increased.

During the 1970s, manufacturers steadily increased working temperatures, by developing special materials for use in the turbine blades. Above about 900°C, it becomes necessary to cool the first turbine stage to maintain metal temperatures within material capability, in terms of both hot strength and oxidation resistance. Air cooling is universally used for this purpose. The extraction of cooling air from the compressor and its re-injection causes a loss of performance, which must be offset by an increase in temperature (typically about 100°C) before a net benefit is obtained. Pressure ratios have also been increased, reflecting a wish to make best use of the improved temperature capability.

At pressure ratios of greater than 6:1, the simple axial compressor has a limited speed range over which it can be matched to the turbine; at low speeds the front stages become stalled. This can be overcome by using variable geometry. An essential part of any new engine development is a compressor test programme, which requires a substantial investment in facilities. Current designs include models having a pressure ratio of 12:1 and a cycle temperature of 1,000 to 1,100°C.

Turbine cooling is another aspect that requires comprehensive theoretical and experimental verification programmes.

The ability to move power generation easily and quickly between location is sometimes required. Mobile packages based on gas turbines can be provided, including all control and safety gear. The only site work required is the provision of a hardstanding, fuel, and connections to an exhaust stack or silencer, and to the electrical system.

For the immediate future, the virtues of the simple cycle machine will ensure its continuing development, with emphasis on improvements in thermal efficiency and emissions control. Aircraft engines already use externally film-cooled blades, and industrial versions are in service. This technique would allow a cycle temperature of over 1,300°C.

Manufacturing cost is strongly dependent on the number and size of components. Blading may now be operated in the supersonic regime with little or no performance penalty giving significant reductions in size and number of stages. Better understanding and methods of predicting three dimensional flow will bring improved component efficiencies.

An alternative route to improved thermal efficiency is the use of a heat exchanger in the recuperative cycle. Adding a recuperator loses several per cent of power. This, and the cost of the extra hardware, increase the capital cost per installed kW. Where a premium fuel is to be used, the better fuel consumption may provide a pay-back, but in many cases factors other than fuel cost prevail. Further improvements in the thermodynamic cycle may be made by sacrificing simplicity. For example, intercooling can be added to the compression process. Although this has little effect on efficiency, it can raise specific power by 30 to 60 per cent. Combining this with recuperation raises power and efficiency.

Heat recovery from industrial gas turbines is commonplace, both for the combined cycle already mentioned, and for the provision of process heat. In the best schemes, 80 per cent of the energy content of the fuel can be employed usefully.

Most industrial gas turbines are designed for, and run on, clean fuels such as diesel oil or natural gas. Direct combustion of crude oil, or oil residues having low ash contents, is possible on larger machines, provided adequate attention is given to appropriate design of fuelling and combustion systems. The problem of fuel ash corrosion of the turbine blades is closely related to metal temperature; the use of air cooling has allowed cycle temperature to rise to more economic levels while maintaining acceptable blade life. However, it is often necessary to de-rate machines working on non-standard fuels. The ash deposition problem in small machines is severe, and clean fuels may be the only viable solution.

There are extensive combustion development activities in the field of emissions reduction. This requires the study of complex inter-actions of engine systems to achieve "DLN" (dry low NO_x - nitrogen oxides) without sacrificing performance, endurance or handling characteristics. Natural gas is the preferred fuel for optimum performance, but diesel oil can be an alternative for emergency operation.

System performance with non-standard fuels can be predicted with reasonable accuracy. Potential for emissions reduction varies with fuel composition; in general it should be expected that bio-oil will give a higher level of NO_x than results from the use of diesel oil.

4.3 New concepts

Electricity is a form of energy which has many uses, and it does not cause environmental pollution at the point of use. Emissions are produced at the power station, where they are easier to control. Although electricity cannot be stored, more or less extended supply grids are already in place in many countries. These are used to balance regional peaks of supply and demand of electricity. The large national grids are generally powered by large, centralised generating sets, running on fossil or nuclear fuels.

The use of biomass as a fuel for electricity requires alternatives to the established concept of centralised energy production, to take into account the particular requirements of the raw material and to take advantage of new opportunities. Nevertheless, use of existing supply grids should not be ruled out.

Biomass has a low energy density compared with, say, coal. Also, the cultivation of sufficient biomass to make significant contributions to power production would entail the use of large areas of land. It is obvious, therefore, that transport must be a main cost factor when large-scale power plants are considered. Decentralized, smaller-scale power plants, which could obtain their fuel material from surrounding plantations and supply electricity into an existing grid, can be seen as a promising alternative. Additional benefits may arise if the power plant can be used in combined cycle and located close to demand for process heat or district heating, so that the waste heat can be used for those purposes.

Historically, in the power range below 1 MW, the engines used for power generators have been, almost exclusively, of the reciprocating type. To operate these using biomass as a source of liquid fuel, and to achieve satisfactory performance and acceptable emissions, the biomass would have to be converted to a high-quality fuel (e.g. ethanol or diesel-substitute), which would be prohibitively expensive on a limited scale.

Gas turbines at a size of over a few MW are cheaper to install and run than reciprocating engines. Gas turbines can be operated on fuels having low calorific values, but the simple cycle efficiency of conventional turbines in this power range is lower than that of piston engines. However, it is more common to use the gas turbines in combined cycle to make use of the high quality exhaust heat. The first step of one concept applicable to decentralised energy supply using a biomass fuel is therefore, the development of small, high efficiency gas turbines at competitive costs. It has been suggested that such gas turbines could be run on dried and powdered biomass.

This concept is being examined by a consortium of the Italian State electricity company (ENEL), Daimler-Benz and Ferruzzi-Fertec, who are advised by Prof. Stander of the Munich Polytechnic Institute. They are investigating the technical and economic feasibility of combustion of powdered biomass in a 400 kW gas turbine in a co-generation plant.

The firing of biomass powder in a test rig combustor has shown that the alternative fuel material can be fed to, and burnt in, a gas turbine and that gaseous emissions comply with applicable limits. Nevertheless, key problems remaining to be investigated are the economical comminution of the biomass, the collection and disposal of ash, and the further development of ceramic parts to increase the efficiency of the gas turbine by operating it at higher temperatures. At the present state of knowledge, the use of ceramic parts limits the capacity of individual turbines, but there is already some relevant experience available from research on small stationary turbines and turbines for passenger cars; this has to be transferred to the new concept.

First results are encouraging for commercial exploitation. The investigations should be extended to cover a wider area of technical possibilities.

4.4 Integrated systems

Three issues have been linked in the literature with the need to develop renewables:

(a) Oil: prices and security of supply.

(b) Agricultural sector support in the EC and US.

(c) Global Warming and non-fossil energy technologies

These driving forces are quite distinct, and a response to one perceived threat or economic challenge may well act against the dictates of another.

4.4.1 *Oil.* Oil's strategic importance rests primarily on the vital role of transportation fuels in a modern economy. There is widespread agreement that oil reserves are sufficient to meet demand well into the next century, with only modest price increases. Nevertheless, as almost 80 per cent of the world's crude reserves are concentrated in the Middle East region, the potential for surprises always exists, even in the short/medium term, and higher prices could result from an effective producer cartel or political instabilities. In the longer term, oil prices will inevitably rise with physical supply constraints, and energy sector investment could shift to alternative resources.

This would not automatically create a role for biomass: natural gas, heavy oil/tar sands, oil shales and coal may well be lower-cost alternatives for the production of liquid transportation fuels. The analytical problem in the context of public policy formulation is to establish a cost hierarchy indicating the order in which the various resources and technical options would be brought on stream (and achieve a given rate of return) as the wholesale prices of oil products rise. Policies promoting high cost options would make little sense in this context.

32

4.4.2 *Agriculture Sector Support.* Overproduction in the EC and US agriculture sectors can be similarly examined. Cereals production in the EC is currently 160 to 170 million tonnes and rises year by year. In contrast, the internal market is closer to 130 million tonnes and relatively static. Surplus production is sold on world markets, at prices substantially lower than EC internal support levels. The economic effects of this policy are well documented and include negative impacts on the EC-US trading relationship and on Third World agriculture. A range of solutions has been proposed including:

(a) Removal of EC price supports; perhaps substituting income supports as alternative means to satisfy rural policy objectives.

(b) Application of production quotas, limiting cereals output to Community internal demand; eliminating those aspects of current policy which are most controversial and damaging internationally.

(c) Use of surplus cereals to produce ethanol for automotive energy use.

Each of these options has strengths and weaknesses. The first two could create serious disruption in the agriculture sector if the transition is not managed carefully; but may result in lower land prices, reducing one of the major obstacles to energy cropping in the EC. It has been estimated that up to 14 million hectares could be taken out of mainstream agricultural production. Some of this land might then be available for energy production, commercial forestry, or, if the necessary public ownership mechanisms could be set up, a range of public amenity or semi-commercial forestry applications.

The carbohydrate-based ethanol option seems merely to compound existing problems of agricultural policy. It would be inefficient both in economic terms and, if it became a focus of public policy, from the carbon mitigation standpoint. It does, however, have superficial appeal in that the technology is well known, and the volume of ethanol represented by current cereals surpluses could be accommodated by blending ten per cent by volume in the EC gasoline pool. Intensive cereals production would maintain the status quo in land use, and surpluses would continue to rise - in step with the subsidies necessary to place of the order of 10 million tonnes of fuel alcohol within the EC gasoline pool.

4.4.3 *Global Warming.* The atmospheric carbon issue remains, for the time being, a matter of speculation. However, if in the future, governments enact policies which effectively place a price on the use of the atmosphere as a sink for fossil carbon emissions - for example by means of carbon taxes - the economics of energy crops could receive a boost.

The analytical problem for policy-makers in this case, is to establish a cost ordering for the various resources and technical options, including a given rate of return, plus a term representing the hypothetical (or real) costs of emitting fossil carbon. This cost ordering will depend on the size of the carbon term.

Assuming that the relative costs of biomass energy crops can be brought down into a range that makes them competitive, either in a free market scenario or in a "carbon-constrained" scenario, then there are strong a priori reasons to suggest that effort should focus on the power sector as opposed to transportation fuels. (Liquid fuel production technologies currently under development - based on lignocellulose, not carbohydrates - may weaken this conclusion, but are unlikely to reverse it in the foreseeable future.) First, the wholesale market for electricity commands higher prices than the market for liquid automotive fuels, and it is more easily penetrated by biomass if an unmodified free market prevails. This point is elaborated below. Second, as shown in a recent publication from Oak Ridge National Laboratory (Wright, Graham, Turhollow and English, 1991), the greatest carbon benefit per unit of wood can be obtained by following the electricity - as opposed to the ethanol - production route. Any future taxes on fossil carbon emissions would give additional weight to the commercial argument for power generation based on sustainable biomass production.

4.4.4 *Policy Priorities.* Precision is required in defining objectives if society is to avoid the burdens of expensive and ineffective policy. Ultimately, biomass may be competitive with fossil fuels in some areas, without any enabling policy, and indeed the Short Rotation Woody Crop (SRWC) programme in the US aims for this goal. Nevertheless, biomass is currently able to compete only in restricted niches of the energy market, and changes in public policy would be required to promote biomass on a broader scale. Policy makers will need to be quite clear on their objectives, and on the full implications of enabling policy to ensure that the ensuing changes are socially beneficial.

4.5.5 *Feedstock costs.* Biomass feedstocks suitable for energy applications fall into three broad categories:

(a) relatively pure carbohydrates such as sugar and starch

(b) vegetable oils

(c) heterogeneous woody materials, collectively termed lignocellulose.

The following discussion applies primarily to lignocellulose, although carbohydrates and oils are briefly dealt with in Section 4.5.8. The currency of international energy markets is the US dollar and, at the time of writing, 1 ECU is equivalent to 1.14 $US. As an approximation, therefore, dollar and ECU units can be interchanged without distorting the logic of the discussion. Close to source, the cost of useful energy in the form of lignocellulose can be competitive with fossil fuels. Many large scale forestry operations, particularly in tropical and sub-tropical climate zones, quote into-plant costs in the range of $20 to 40 per bone dry tonne (BDT) of pulp wood, or approximately $1 to 2 per GJ. This low cost range results principally from low land prices, combined with high growth rates of plants in favourable climates.

The SRWC programme, managed by the Oak Ridge National Laboratory in the US, promises similar costs for temperate zone energy crops. Results based on limited trials suggest costs in the range of $40 to 60 per BDT ($2 to 3 per GJ) are feasible in the short to medium term, wherever medium to good crop-land is available in the US at a sufficiently low price. The goal for this research programme is to reduce costs by the year 2010 below $40 per BDT. This may well be realistic because SRWC yields higher than those implicit in the target are already being achieved in the best small plot trials.

Work is less advanced in Europe, but shows similar longer term promise. However, the price of land in Europe, which reflects its income-generating potential in alternative uses (and a high population density), is a major obstacle in energy crop economics. Residues from agriculture and forestry can often be concentrated in large quantities at costs ranging from $10 to 20 per BDT (around $0.5 to 1 per GJ) for sawmill residues, or $30 to 45 per BDT (around $2 to 3 per GJ) for cereal crop residues.

Starch and sugar feedstocks that are suitable for fermentation are somewhat more expensive, ranging from $100 to 200 per tonne ($6 to 12 per GJ) for US maize and EC wheat respectively. Oilseed rape leaves EC farms around $350 to 500 per tonne, and has an extractable oil content of 40 to 42 per cent; giving oil production costs around $850 to 1,250 per tonne ($23 to 34 per GJ). Processors receive "crushing subsidies" to ensure that the product is competitive with other vegetable oils.

4.4.6 *Commercial options*. There are three main options to divert biomass into commercial energy channels. These are:

(a) solid fuels (underboiler/kiln);

(b) liquid fuels (automotive);

(c) power generation.

The value of energy in each of these markets is compared in Figure 4.1 with the costs of the various feedstocks. The production costs of alternative fuels are frequently compared with the retail prices of oil products, which include substantial tax elements. The economic distortions implicit in such a comparison can be justified only in exceptional circumstances - for example, involving urgent considerations of security of supply. The original rationale for using excise duty waivers to promote maize-based ethanol in the USA was based on this logic. With the benefit of hindsight, many commentators consider that this programme has not fulfilled a real need, and continued funding is aimed largely at dependent interests in agriculture and the corn milling industry.

4.4.7 *Solid fuels.* Underboiler fuel prices are set directly by competition between coal, fuel oil and natural gas. Internationally traded steam coal is typically priced between $45 to 60 per tonne ($1.8 to 2.4 per GJ) and, with substantial surplus production capacity, varies little with routine fluctuations in oil prices. However, the EC coal sector is somewhat complicated by protection and subsidies, and prices vary markedly between locations and customers. Fuel oil and natural gas prices tend to shift in response to the cost of crude oil as indicated in Figure 4.1.

Solid biomass fuels have a low energy density, particularly in the raw state, so commercial opportunities in kiln or underboiler applications are limited by energy market economics, particularly transport costs, to locations close to the point of biomass production. Niche opportunities often involve specific local factors such as the need to dispose of process residues, or the availability of wastes. Sometimes investment grants are available for specialised combustion systems for which conversion costs can be high. Extending the application of solid biomass fuels to meet local underboiler requirements could stimulate further upgrading of fuel oil into the transportation sector which is less easily penetrated by renewables.

4.4.8 *Liquid fuels.* A higher-value option is the automotive market, that is, gasoline and gas oil (or diesel). Wholesale product prices (excluding excise duties and sales taxes, which make up a substantial proportion of pump prices in many countries) are typically 1.2 to 1.4 times the price of crude oil in volume terms. In recent years, the wholesale price range for automotive fuels has been $4 to 6 per GJ. In the early 1980s, when oil prices peaked at around $(1990) 60 per barrel, or more than three times recent levels, the automotive market was seen as the logical target for biomass conversion processes. Sizeable commercial programmes were initiated, most notably in Brazil and the USA. In 1989, Brazil produced over nine million tonnes of fuel ethanol from cane sugar, at a cost estimated in 1982 at more than $300 per tonne, equivalent to $12/GJ.

36

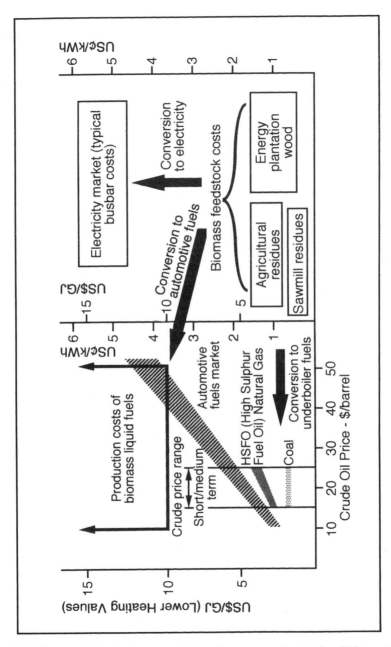

Figure 4.1. Biomass fuels in the perspective of energy markets (after Elliot and Booth, 1991)

The ethanol programme in the USA has grown to around two million tonnes per annum, based on maize. In 1987, the production costs of this industry were estimated (Marrow, Coombs and Lees, 1987) to be in the range of $500 to 550 per tonne ($20 to 22 per GJ). By comparison, in mid 1991, ethanol had an energy value in the wholesale gasoline market of little more than $5 per GJ, so these programmes have required considerable government support. Such support is provided, for example, in the form of excise duty waivers.

In the USA, a federal excise duty of six cents a gallon of gasoline is, at the time of writing, waived for gasohol containing ten per cent of ethanol. This amounts to a subsidy of 60 cents per US gallon or almost $200 per tonne of ethanol ($8 per GJ). Many US states also waive their own excise duties on gasohol, contributing similar amounts to the overall subsidy. A US Department of Agriculture report (Sperling, 1989), estimated that twenty-nine states contributed $302.5 million to ethanol fuel in 1985, and that the federal gasoline tax exemption caused a loss of about $500 million per year from the Federal Highway Trust Fund - for a total of $800 million in 1985.

The dominant cost of ethanol produced from sugar and starch crops is the feedstock, and work is proceeding on cheaper alternatives. Lignocellulose, from energy forestry and agricultural and forest industry residues, has long been targeted as a low-cost feedstock for biomass liquids production. However, nature has formulated lignocellulose to withstand both physical and chemical attack over the long lifetime of a tree, and it is not an easy feedstock to process. The technology for converting lignocellulose becomes significantly more complex than that required for sugar and starch feedstocks and, as a consequence, capital costs dominate the process economics.

Economies of scale force a requirement for larger plant capacities, which may in turn limit the use of low-cost residues and increase the transport cost element of plantation-grown feedstock. Nevertheless, in the tight oil market of the early 1980s, many organisations, including Shell, worked on processes to upgrade lignocellulose to higher-value commercial fuels as substitutes for conventional gasoline and diesel. The Shell research, on hydrolysis/fermentation and hydrothermal upgrading, suggested that it is unlikely that ethanol or high quality, automotive-grade hydrocarbons can be produced from biomass for substantially less than $10 to 12 per GJ, several times higher than the mid 1991 ex-refinery price of equivalents derived from crude oil.

A more recent estimate (Solar Energy Research Institute - SERI, 1990) suggests that if all critical developmental hurdles are cleared, costs as low as $8 to 9 per GJ (LHV) might be feasible by the year 2020. Assuming that a practical efficiency of conversion from lignocellulose to ethanol of 450 litres per tonne of dry feedstock is achievable (Hall, Mynick and Williams, 1990), then feedstock costing $40 per tonne ($2 per GJ) will contribute $112 per tonne ethanol ($4.5 per GJ) to the cost of the product. This implies that the cost of operation and maintenance, together with capital recovery will not exceed $3.5 to 4.5 per GJ. The capital cost of such a plant, with a capacity of 200,000 tonnes a year, is likely to be of the order of $100 million, or $500 per annual tonne. Assuming a 20 per cent capital charge, capital recovery (including corporate taxes) would absorb $100 a tonne ($4 per GJ). It therefore seems unlikely that actual plants could improve significantly on SERI's estimate of achievable costs.

4.4.9 Biomass power generation. Electricity is a high value market, with wholesale prices typically about 5 cents per kilowatt hour (kWh) at the power plant. This is equivalent to $14 per GJ, or $85 per barrel of oil equivalent, or around three times the wholesale price of automotive fuels in mid-1991. Market value alone provides a powerful rationale for looking at the potential of biomass energy in this sector.

Steam power plants of around 25 MW are already used to generate power from agricultural and forest industry residues. In the USA, almost 9 GW of capacity is operated in situations offering a combination of low feedstock costs and high electricity prices. Under the terms of the US Public Utilities Regulatory Policies Act (PURPA) of 1978, power utilities are obliged to buy electricity offered by independent generators at prices that reflect avoided costs - the costs that would be incurred if the utility provided the additional power.

In the early 1980s, such costs often ran as high as 9 US cents per kWh and, at these guaranteed prices, there was a rush of developers to sign contracts. However, as avoided cost levels dropped towards 5 US cents per kWh, the flow of new biomass power projects has declined markedly, because conventional steam cycle plants are handicapped by a combination of low efficiency and high specific investment cost at a scale suited to biomass applications.

4.5.10 New biomass power generation technology. Recent assessments of emerging technologies suggest that power plants of a modest scale could achieve thermal efficiencies in excess of 40 per cent within a few years (eventually reaching 50 per cent or more), combined with capital costs well below those of comparable conventional biomass plants. A number of technological concepts are promising but one of the front-runners is based on work carried out by General Electric on behalf of the USA Department of Energy. This study (Corman, 1986) examined the technological options to improve the economic performance of coal gasification/power generation. Essentially, it was proposed to couple air-blown (rather than oxygen-blown) gasifiers with hot gas clean-up and steam-injected gas turbines (STIG) or, when the technology is developed, intercooled, steam-injected gas turbines (ISTIG). This configuration appears to offer the combined advantages of high efficiency and low capital cost on a comparatively small scale (100 MW$_e$ or less).

Lignocellulose, with its negligible sulfur content, low ash, high volatiles content and high char reactivity, would be an ideal feedstock in such a system. The high efficiency and absence of major scale economies over 100 MW mean that the technology could be implemented in projects at a scale appropriate to biomass feedstocks, including low cost residues as well as more expensive energy crops.

A recent Shell study (Elliott and Booth, 1990), suggested that such plants might ultimately be built at a cost of around $1,200 to 1,300 per kw, with a thermal efficiency (based on the lower heating value) in excess of 42 per cent. Whilst this represents a significant advance on existing technologies, feedstock remains a problem in the EC context. Within the terms of reference of this study, it was difficult to develop a credible short term scenario in which energy crops give adequate returns to the farmer, whilst producing fuels competitive with fossil sources. It seems likely, therefore, that any early ventures in the EC will utilise residues produced in agricultural and forestry operations.

The position of EC energy crops could change in the longer term with increases in the prices of fossil energies, yield increases for energy crops, or major changes in the fiscal regime - particularly relating to fossil carbon emission, or other government measures to promote biomass as a source of commercial energy. Novel arrangements such as those recently introduced in the UK power sector (the so-called "Non-Fossil Fuel Obligation" or NFFO), could be adapted to promote the necessary investment, not only in appropriate power generation technologies, but also in the development of high yield energy crops.

Legislation dealing with privatisation of the UK power sector not only opens the network to independent generators, but also obliges the regional electricity companies in England and Wales to secure stipulated quantities of electricity from non-fossil sources - the NFFO. The programme is funded by a levy on fossil-based electricity and is intended primarily to support the nuclear power sector, which remains in public ownership. Nevertheless, the NFFO involves a tariff structure (equivalent to around 10 US cents per kWh for some projects) designed to bring forward limited quantities of power from a range of renewable resources; and should provide operating data and the necessary experience on which to base future expansion of the programme.

Editors' note: Specific investment costs vary widely ($1,200 to 3000 Kw) depending on scale (1 to 100 MW) and design efficiency (15 to 30 per cent).

5. Techno-economic analysis

5.1 Costs of biomass pyrolysis liquids production and upgrading

5.1.1 Small scale systems. The gross and net costs of a small scale pyrolysis system for producing crude pyrolysis oil are shown in Table 5.1. This is based on the assumptions that properly prepared feed stock is delivered to the site and used immediately with no reception, storage, or pretreatment operations required, and only minimal handling. This, therefore, represents the most optimistic cost scenario and is restricted to small scale operations of probably not more than 2 tonnes per hour. It does show, however, the dominance of feed cost in the total cost, and also permits exploration of the effects of different costs and fiscal incentives. The following credits are expected to be applicable:

(a) a premium for low sulfur emissions;

(b) socio-economic and environmental credits associated with labour

(c) exemption from carbon tax, and subvention from tax revenues, to support solutions to the carbon dioxide emissions problem.

Other studies have more thoroughly explored the economics of small scale pyrolysis systems for liquids (Bridgwater, 1991a and 1991b).

5.1.2 Techno-economic assessment of large scale systems. A project has been initiated to examine the full range of direct liquefaction technologies for liquid fuel production from biomass, which includes further development of a techno-economic computer simulation programme to carry out objective and consistent evaluations of alternative pyrolysis and upgrading technologies.

The scope and methodology of the project are outlined here; details have already been published (Bridgwater and Double, 1990). The programme is referred to as AMBLE - Aston Model of Biomass to Liquids for Energy. The technologies, process routes and products to which the methodology is applicable are summarised in Figure 5.1.

For the analysis of these processes, a complete and integrated process route is considered, from wood delivered to the factory gate through to an end product, as would be the case in a real and significant conversion facility, typically processing from 200 to 1,000 tonnes a day of dry biomass. All necessary pretreatment steps of reception, storage, screening, drying and comminution are included, as well as the conversion and upgrading steps.

41

Table 5.1. Production costs of bio-oil at an output of 1 tonne or 10 tonnes an hour. The net cost represents the reference value for comparison with crude oil imported and de-sulfurised to 0.1 per cent

	ECU per tonne of bio-oil 1 t/h	ECU per tonne of oil equiv 1 t/h	$/bbl of oil equiv[1] 1 t/h	ECU per tonne of oil equiv 10 t/h	$/bbl of oil equiv 10 t/h
COSTS					
Biomass at 50 ECU per tonne[2]	71.4	160.7	30.7	160.7	30.7
Investment costs	14.3	32.2	6.1	16.9	3.2
Conversion costs	32.2	72.4	13.8	31.9	6.1
GROSS COST	117.9	265.3	50.6	209.5	41.0
CREDITS					
Desulfurisation[3]	32.6	73.5	14.0	73.5	14.0
Fiscal incentives[4]	16.3	36.8	7.0	36.8	7.0
NET COST	69.0	155.0	29.6	99.3	20.0
Char sales if available[4]	7.5	16.9	3.2	16.9	3.2
Net cost with char sales[5]	61.5	138.1	26.4	82.3	16.8

Notes:
[1]Conversion at $1.14/ECU at July 1991, and 7.2 barrels per tonne.
[2]At a yield of 70 per cent by weight.
[3]De-sulfurised to 0.1 per cent sulfur. This is the current (1991) premium for a low sulfur fuel oil.
[4]Product taxation through manpower salaries, balance of payments improvements from reduced imports, and avoided losses in refineries.
[5]This assumes a yield of 10 per cent by weight of charcoal, having a Higher Heating Value of 30 MJ/kg. If this charcoal is not required for drying feedstock it can be sold, and it is (conservatively) credited at the same value as biomass cost on a heating value basis.

5.1.2.1 *Process steps.* The overall system is considered to be made up of a number of steps, through which the material being processed passes sequentially as outlined in Figure 5.1. By combining the results of models of all of the steps, the performance of the whole process can be determined (Bridgwater and Double, 1991). Each process step is treated as an integrated unit. Calculations within each step can be as complex as necessary to give the required accuracy. Each step is a self-contained operation which includes all inputs and actions necessary for it to function, including requirements for capital cost and utilities.

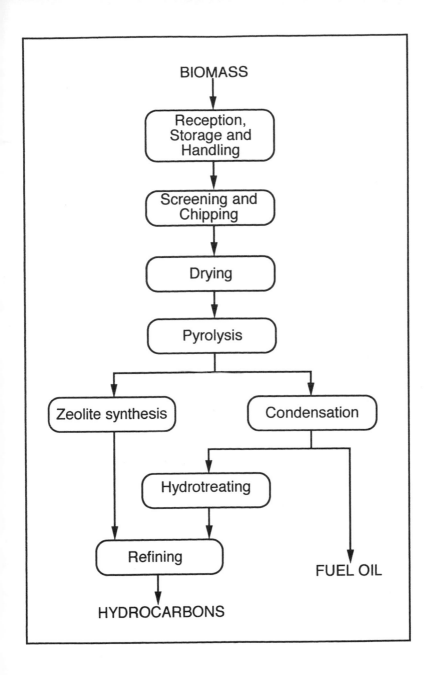

Figure 5.1. Processing routes for pyrolysis liquids.

5.1.2.2 Process synthesis and programme output. The processes are constructed by linking the steps in logical sequences based on specifications for feedstock, product and, where relevant, conversion technology.

5.1.2.3 Utilities. The utilities are represented in the models by imports, exports or surpluses using pooling arrangements. Each utility is debited or credited at the market rate. Optimisation of energy use is not currently considered.

5.1.2.4 Outline mass balances for liquid fuels production. To compare different systems in terms of mass balance and energy efficiency, two conceptual processes are summarised in Table 5.2, based on either hydrotreating or zeolite upgrading. Both processes start from wet biomass in the forest, and produce increasingly refined, and hence more valuable, products: pyrolysis oil, crude hydrocarbons, aromatics and refined hydrocarbons.

The data for hydrotreating yields is derived from a the results of a cooperative study, carried out under the auspices of the International Energy Agency, of the technoeconomics of liquid fuel synthesis (Beckman, Elliott, Gevert, Hornell, Kjellstrom, Ostman, Solantausta and Tulenheimo, 1990), which was based bench scale research carried out at Battelle PNL (Baker and Elliott, 1988). The data for zeolite upgrading is based on small scale experimentation at the Solar Energy Research Institute (Scahill and Diebold, 1988). Yields for hydrotreated products are set at 90 per cent; these products are of relatively low value and can either be used for blending or be refined to a conventional product. Zeolite products are highly aromatic and have a high intrinsic value for blending (or for chemicals production) and are thus ascribed a (conservative) positive refining yield.

5.1.2.5 Mass balances and costs for liquid fuels production by hydrotreating and zeolites. Tables 5.3 and 5.4 give mass balances and production cost estimates for both methods of upgrading on an overall and incremental basis. These based on chipped wood delivered to the factory gate, and include all costs for a complete process including reception, storage, handling, pretreatment conversion, upgrading and product storage, as shown in Figure 5.1.

These tables have been prepared on the basis that the additional step of refining is required for upgrading by hydrotreating (but not with zeolite synthesis) because of the lower quality of hydrotreated product. Even so, there is no significant difference in the costs and yields of the refined hydrotreated oil and the aromatic oil from zeolites under similar conditions.

Table 5.2. Typical mass balances and yields in conversions to liquid products (dry wood = 100 by weight)

Stage in process		Mass balance (%)	
		Hydrotreating	Zeolites
Biomass production, wet wood at a moisture content of 50 per cent by weight, wet basis		200	200
Wood dried to a moisture content not exceeding 10 per cent, wet basis		110	110
Size reduction to less than 3mm		110	110
Flash pyrolysis to crude (wet) bio-oil at a yield of 70 per cent by weight of dry wood		70	70
Upgrading to crude hydrocarbons by hydrotreating at a yield of 37 per cent by weight of bio-oil		26	-
Refining to gasoline and/or diesel at a yield of 90 per cent by weight of crude hydrocarbons		23	-
Upgrading to aromatics by zeolites at a yield of 21 per cent by weight of dry, ash-free wood		-	21
Refining to gasoline at a yield of 105 per cent by weight of aromatics		-	22
Products		Overall yields - percentages	
Pyrolysis oil	mass basis	70	70
	energy basis	67	67
Partially hydrotreated bio-oil	mass basis	48	-
	energy basis	60	-
Crude hydrocarbons	mass basis	26	21
	energy basis	56	47
Refined hydrocarbons	mass basis	23	22
	energy basis	52	47

Note: For electricity production, if crude bio-oil is found to be unsuitable then a partially upgraded or stabilised fuel might be acceptable which would be cheaper than a fully hydrotreated bio-oil. This concept has not been proven, but is currently (1991) being investigated.

Table 5.3. Production costs for hydrotreating and refining pyrolysis oil from biomass in a large-scale, integrated conversion process. *Basis:* 1,000 tonnes a day of dry, ash-free wood feedstock delivered to the factory gate at a price of 50 ECU per tonne in a West European location in 1990. See also note at bottom of table 5.2.

Product	Yield - per cent by weight	Cost - ECU per tonne of product	Higher Heating Value - GJ per tonne	Cost - ECU per GJ in product	Cost - ECU per tonne of oil equivalent
Dry, ash-free wood feedstock	100	50	20	2.5	108
Pyrolysis oil output (including water)	70	109	19	5.6	246
Hydrotreated bio-oil	26	384	42	9.1	393
Partially upgraded bio-oil	48	-	-	-	-
Refined hydrotreated bio-oil	23	440	44	10.0	430
For comparison, crude oil at:					
$20 a barrel	-	126	43	2.9	126
$40 a barrel	-	126	43	5.8	252

Figure 5.2 shows the effect of feed cost variations on product cost from the two processes, and contrasts these against the costs of fuels made from crude oil. The plotted lines of fuel cost versus feed cost are not parallel because the products are of different quality; the incremental cost of upgrading based on a hydrotreated oil product cannot simply be added to the pyrolysis oil cost, because the bases are different. The same applies to refining, although the effect is less noticeable because the products are of similar quality. For gasoline production using zeolites, a similar effect occurs, although in practice, aromatics production cannot be independent of pyrolysis, as a close-coupled operation is essential.

The effects of allowing for credits of 3.0 ECU/GJ associated with the use of low sulfur oil; of socio-economic contributions resulting from the production, processing and use of biomass; and of environmental and other aspects is shown in Figure 5.3.

Table 5.4. Production costs for pyrolysis with zeolite synthesis. *Basis:* 1,000 tonnes a day of dry, ash-free wood feedstock delivered to the factory gate at a price of 50 ECU per tonne in a West European location in 1990.

Product	Yield - per cent by weight	Cost - ECU per tonne of product	Higher Heating Value - GJ per tonne	Cost - ECU per GJ in product	Cost - ECU per tonne of oil equivalent
Dry, ash-free wood feedstock	100	50	20	2.5	108
Pyrolysis oil output (including water)	70	109	19	5.6	246
Aromatic output	21	350	44	7.9	342
Gasolin output	22	337	44	7.8	329
For comparison: crude oil at $20 per barrel $1.14 = 1 ECU	-	126	43	2.9	126

5.1.3 Electricity. Production costs of electricity are shown in Figure 5.4 for two scales of operation (1 and 10 MW$_e$ export capacity), and at two levels of fuel conversion efficiency (30 and 50 per cent) in terms of fuel fed to the turbine, to cover the full range of potential electricity generation technologies. The lower figure of 30 per cent represents traditional generation modes, where fuel (eg bio-oil) is burned in a boiler to raise steam, and the higher figure represents a target for combined cycle operation, or similar high performance conversion again fuelled with bio-oil or upgraded bio-oil. This latter alternative is likely to be viable only at larger scales of operation, say above 10 MW$_e$, due to decreasing efficiencies and increasing costs as the capacity reduces.

5.1.4 Conclusions. The performance and cost estimates for both crude pyrolysis liquids and refined hydrocarbon products show that, while the crude liquids can be economic at low feedstock costs, refined hydrocarbons are still not competitive without credits for low sulfur, environmental contributions and socio-economic contributions. As feedstock cost is the major cost item, any process that can utilise waste materials having low inherent costs will have the best chance to show economic viability in the short term.

47

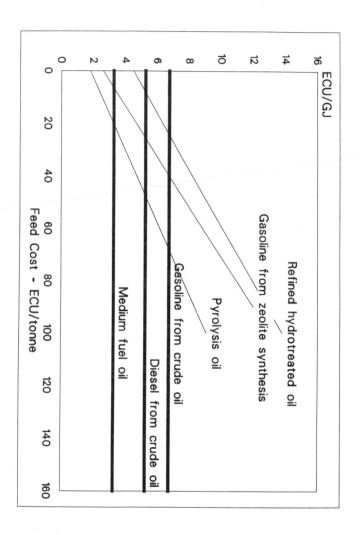

Figure 5.2 Effects of costs of feedstock on the products of pyrolysis and subsequent upgrading, against the costs of fuels made from crude oil.

48

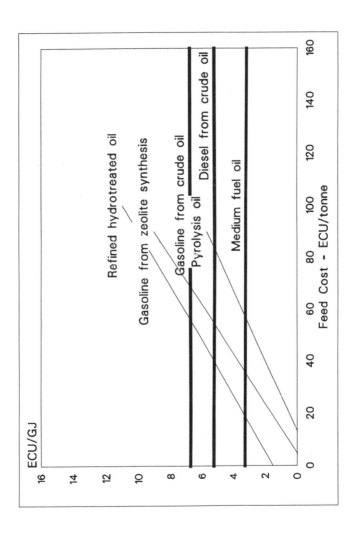

Figure 5.3 Effects of allowing credits for environmental and socio-economic factors on the cost of crude and refined pyrolysis products.

49

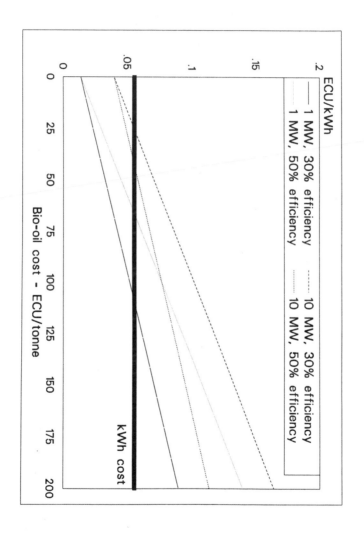

Figure 5.4 Costs of making electricity from bio-oil

5.2. Costs of electricity generation

5.2.1. Introduction The price of electricity generated from purpose grown biomass is strongly dependent on feedstock costs and the efficiency of power generation. A simple analysis of the relationships between biomass production costs (including the impact of support measures), plant yields and conversion efficiencies is presented. This can be used to identify the key areas where research and development activities will reduce the costs of generating electricity from biomass. This is necessary at present in order to make such activity competitive with electricity from fossil fuel sources or that generated on at present on a more restricted scale from wastes (including municipal solid waste), agricultural residues and landfill gas - at present the major alternative fuels used. In particular the UK has placed an emphasis on electricity from landfill gas and Denmark in generating power from biogas derived in large plant. France, Germany, Holland and Italy combust significant quantities of domestic and other wastes in cogeneration facilities. Although such use generates an income which may be used to offset waste disposal costs, or provide commercial opportunities for small companies on a local basis, the potential generating capacity is limited by the availability of suitable wastes. Furthermore, the amount of combustible waste may be expected to decrease, as would the availability of landfill gas, as waste management changes under pressures resulting from environmental consideration and associated legislation, which includes proposed directives from the CEC on both *Landfill Practice* and *Packaging*.

5.2.2. Biomass and waste-based electricity generation This concern for waste reduction and increased recycling has already resulted in national legislation in Denmark, Germany and France, whilst other countries have introduced greater control of waste handling - such as the new *Environmental Protection Act* in the UK. At the same time recent changes in the Common Agricultural Policy (CAP) will increase the rate at which land in the EC is taken out of food production, through *set-aside*. Parallel measures controlling nitrogen fertilizer use, ground water quality, milk quotas and so on will also result in lower productivity as well as less manure and straw. The net result will be to limit the potential size of the *electricity-from-waste* industry. Already companies generating power from waste are looking for alternative feedstocks and have considered purpose grown biomass, attracted by the possibility of lower cost biomass production associated with *set-aside* payments. Even so, currently, biomass grown using present systems and converted using conventional small scale steam turbines cannot in general compete with traditional fossil or nuclear sources, unless supported by aid schemes, such as the Non Fossil Fuel Obligation (NFFO) in the UK, or by the existance of a market for the heat produced at the same time, as in Denmark where large cogeneration schemes provide district heating.

5.2.3. Biomass costs and yields In order to obtain a major share of the electricity market waste-based operations will have to evolve into systems using purpose grown biomass, with raw material cost the major factor controlling the rate of growth of the industry. Costs of delivering biomass to the factory gate divide into the costs of production and the costs of harvesting, transport, storage and possibly drying. Costs of production are related to land area rather than the volume or weight of biomass generated, whereas transport and harvest costs are weight or volume related. Consequently, as shown in Figure 5.5, the contribution of feedstock costs to the selling price of electricity is strongly dependent on the yields (tonnes dry matter per hectare). Figure 5.5a, indicates the add-on costs, comprising both fixed and variable costs, together with a transport component and a *farmers' margin*. This can be set at a level which reflects the opportunity cost of alternatives such as wheat, rape or milk production, or in terms of a contribution from *set-aside*. Obviously, large variations occur in both costs and anticipated margins from region to region, reflecting the existing (or displaced) crop, labour rates and so on. Irrespective of the values chosen the basic conclusions remain the same, with a dramatic decrease in fuel costs sustainable yields of more than 15 to 20 tonnes dry weight per hectare per year can be achieved (Figure 5.5b).

To achieve these dry matter yields requires the choice and development of specific crops as indicated in chapter 2 and studied elsewhere (Alexander, 1985). Results from trials are superimposed on Figure 5.5a, indicating the practicality of reaching these fuel costs if such results can be replicated in large scale production systems. In Figure 5.5b agreement is seen with the cost estimates of coppice of around 3.4 ECU/GJ, dropping to around 2 ECU/GJ for the high yielding grasses, and below this when a contribution from *set-aside* is included.

5.2.4 Electricity costs and generating efficiency Small turbines (under 1 MW) using steam from simple combustion of straw or other agricultural waste such as sugar cane bagasse, for which considerable experience and data exists (Paturau 1989, Payne 1991) may be as low as 10 to 15 per cent. Efficiency increases in larger generating plant as more sophisticated generating technology can be utilised (see chapter 4). A combination of greater efficiency and high yields reduces generating costs further (Figure 5.6a), compared to the data considered above assuming a 20% efficiency. Hence, as indicated in Figure 5.6b there is an interaction between the impact of reducing raw material cost by increasing yields and increasing process efficiency. Current research and development activities being supported by the CEC combines both objectives. In particular increased efficiency of conversion at the lower end of the scale, that is for small (decentralised) power plant in the 1 to 10 MW range, together with the use of high yielding plants, would significantly reduce the selling price (Figure 5.7).

52

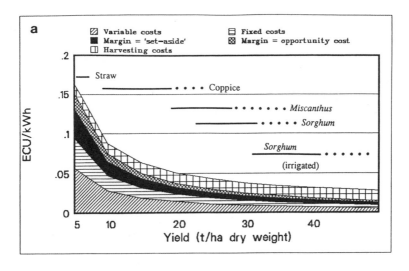

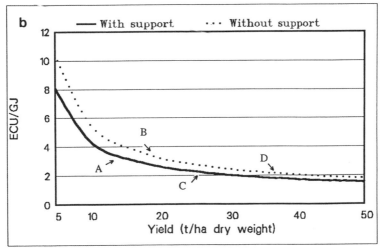

Figure 5.5 a) The impact of dry matter yield on the contribution of biomass fuel costs in electricity generation assuming a conversion efficiency of 20 per cent.

b) The impact of dry matter yield on the cost of biomass fuel used for electricity generation. Arrowed: A and B coppice at 3.4 ECU/GJ, with the value at lower yield compensated for by *set-aside* payments. C and D, biomass produced at around 2 ECU/GJ, if trial productivities of *Miscanthus* or sorghum are achieved on large plantations.

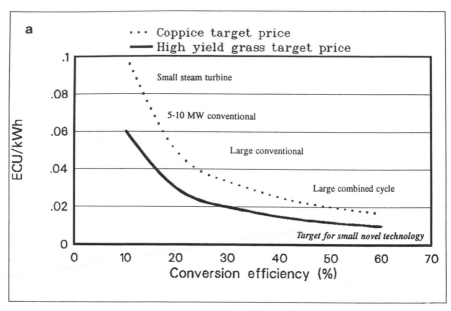

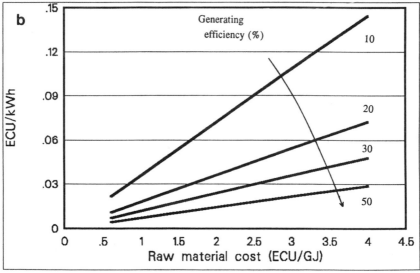

Figure 5.6 a) The impact of the efficiency of electricity generation on the contribution of biomass (fuel) to selling price.

b) Interrelationship between biomass price (reflecting dry matter yield) and conversion efficiency on contribution to electricity selling price.

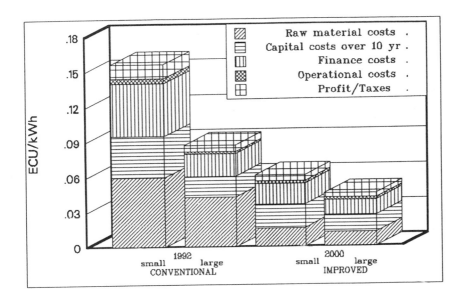

Figure 5.7 Electricity generating costs for small (1-10) MW and large (>20 MW) biomass fuelled systems, for current conventional systems burning straw or waste wood and for improved systems burning purpose grown high yielding crops, if R&D targets are achieved.

5.2.5 Conclusions A substantial reduction in the costs of generating electricity from the combustion of organic raw materials derived from biomass and wastes can be achieved by increasing the yield of plants grown for energy use. If this is combined with technology developments which can achieve conversion efficiencies comparable with those now obtained with large combined-cycle systems based on fossil fuels, then biomass derived electricity can be competitive. In the short term such competitivity is enhanced where *set-aside* payments can be used to reduce the net biomass production cost. In the longer term anticipated improvements in both crop yields and the efficiency of small scale electricity generation using biomass as fuels can significantly improve the economics.

55

6. Emissions - problems and benefits.

At the present time, ECC Directive 88/609 of the European Community Council regulates emissions from new combustion plants having a capacity greater than 50 MW (thermal), but no EC regulations apply to smaller plants. It is, however, probable that future legislation will become more stringent as the attention of the general public and policy makers becomes more focussed on environmental safeguards. From that point of view, the utilisation of biomass for producing electricity introduces some possibilities worthy of consideration.

6.1 *Carbon dioxide.* It is generally recognised that combustion of fossil fuels is responsible for a significant share of the continuously increasing concentration of carbon dioxide (CO_2) in the atmosphere. The global average concentration of CO_2 in the air has increased from 315 ppm in 1958 to 350 ppm now. Every year, about 6 thousand million tonnes of carbon enter the atmosphere as a consequence of the combustion of fossil fuels; only a portion of this can be absorbed, for example by the oceans. The relatively new concept of energy forestry and crops, together with the utilisation of agricultural wastes, could play a relevant role in an integrated scheme to reduce carbon emission and reabsorb atmospheric carbon in the biota. During its relatively fast growing phase, biomass absorbs atmospheric carbon dioxide through photosynthesis. During combustion, it releases CO_2, making a closed cycle, which contributes no net increase in CO_2 to the atmosphere. This is one of the most attractive benefits obtained from utilising biomass, either directly or via fuels derived from processes such as pyrolysis, gasification and liquefaction.

6.2 *Sulfur oxides.* Another benefit gained when biomass is used as a fuel for electricity production arises from the typically very low sulfur contents of biomass (0.1 to 0.2 per cent by mass). Bio-oils can exhibit percentages of less than 0.01 per cent. This is, of course, very favourable for emissions of sulfur oxides (SO_x), which often cause serious pollution from fossil-fuelled power stations, and which can require very complex and expensive desulfurisation processes. The power plants that utilise biomass-based fuel are generally characterized by a relatively small capacity. It would be more difficult and costly to control SO_x emissions at small and scattered plants of this kind, than at large conversion plants. The use of low-sulfur biomass therefore avoids a problem that is otherwise inherent in the use of small, widely spread, electricity generation plant.

6.3 *Nitrogen oxides.* Biomass is less satisfactory in relation to the formation of nitrogen oxides (NO_x) during combustion than it is for SO_x. The content of nitrogen in the biomass feedstock must be controlled, even if it is not very high (about 2 per cent), especially in the case of direct combustion.

In addition, controls are required to obtain pyrolysis oils from biomass having a low nitrogen content (0.2 to 0.6 per cent). 0.2 per cent of fuel-bound nitrogen (FEN) would convert to about 100 ppm by volume of the exhaust from a typical gas turbine, adding to the thermally-produced NO_x and giving a total exhaust NO_x concentration of 250 ppm by volume. The main thermal NO_x compound in flue gas is nitric oxide (NO), contributing over 90 per cent of the total NO_x in most types of combustion processes. There are several ways in which NO_x can be reduced. To prevent the formation of undue levels of NO_x from the oxidation of atmospheric nitrogen during combustion, it is sufficient to reduce:

(a) the combustion temperature to below 1,200 or 1,300°C

(b) the residence time in all high temperature zones.

The control of NO_x formed by the oxidation of nitrogen contained in the fuel could be achieved either by specifying a low nitrogen content, or by decreasing oxygen partial pressures during combustion, but these imply costs, and it is to be expected that there will be a prevalence of fuel NO_x in the total NO_x emissions. Advanced high technology combustion techniques may be necessary to comply with legal limits or, if it proves impracticable to achieve sufficient reduction by combustion control, some post-engine treatment will be needed, such as selective catalytic reaction (SCR).

6.4 *Particulates*. The ash content of biomass is not high (from 2 to 6 per cent), so it is easier to deal with particulate matter than is the case with, say, pulverised coal. The expected small size of the plants running on biomass, and hence the limited volumes of flue gas to be treated, is consistent with the use of fabric filters, instead of the electrostatic precipitators that are usually installed in large, coal-fired power plants. The high efficiency of fabric filters make it possible to limit the particulate emission to very low levels, (say around 3 to 5 mg/Nm^3), without difficulty, and certainly well below the limits of 30 mg/Nm^3 imposed, for example by Italian legislation. The situation could be even better when burning oils derived from biomass, where the ash content could be extremely low (i.e. less than 0.1 per cent). Even so, it will be important to bear in mind the need to limit the content of sodium and potassium to below 1 ppm by mass in bio-oil to be used in a high-temperature gas turbine.

6.5 *Micropollutants*. Levels of micropollutants will be low if the chlorine content of the feedstock biomass is low. However, the residence times at peak temperatures within the combustors of typical gas turbines are too low to destroy some micropollutants. Combustion tests carried out in fluidized beds have recently shown that very low concentrations of dioxins and furans can be achieved even when agricultural wastes are used as fuels.

7. Impacts on the Common Agricultural Policy and on rural development

In the 1980s the Common Agricultural Policy (CAP) resulted in large surpluses of main agricultural products; dealing with these surpluses consumed large parts of the Commission's and Member States' budgets.

To alleviate this problem, a proposal for alternative land use is presented here: large-scale exploitation of biomass for industrial and energy uses, at the level of 600 to 800 million tonnes of oil equivalent a year.

The important benefits to arise from this activity will include: job creation in rural districts, solutions to environmental problems, and technologies applicable in developing countries.

7.1 Introduction

Evaluation of the results of CEC research programmes shows that large scale exploitation of biomass in the medium to long term will offer a significant contribution to resolving the present problems of the CAP. It should be remembered that initial creation and establishment of the CAP were based on political will to ensure adequate supplies of key agricultural products for European consumers.

At the end of the 1970s, excessive amounts of food products accumulated within the EC, because of:

(a) Higher efficiency and output caused by the application of new technologies.

(b) Reduced growth of demand for some foods.

(c) Adjustments to the CAP were not implemented for political reasons.

Consequently, the public stocks of agricultural product in the 7 year period 1984 to 1990 have been fluctuating between 11 and 23 million tonnes a year, costing between 4.6 and 11.3 billion ECU per year (3.7 billion ECU in 1991).

The total Commission expenditure for the CAP was 28 billion ECU in 1989 and 30 billion ECU in 1990 (32 billion ECU is expected for 1991).

In 1990, the CEC and national subsidies were as shown on the next page.

(a) Cereals: 13.4 billion ECU

(b) Olive oil: 3.1 billion ECU

(c) Oil protein crops: 3.2 billion ECU

(d) Sugar beet: 2.6 billion ECU

(e) Vegetables, fruits: 16.8 billion ECU

(f) Wine: 3.8 billion ECU

(g) Meat: 36.2 billion ECU

(h) Others: 2.4 billion ECU

These total 81 billion ECU, or about $100 billion.

Despite this extraordinary financial effort, the CAP has not been able to raise the incomes of the poorest farmers (because the farmers who produce the most, receive the most and therefore inequality has been created among member countries (north to south).

In addition, by subsidising exports, it has created hostility within third world countries.

Storage of milk and butter, wheat and beef costs 56, 31 and 18 million ECU/week. Total storage costs are estimated at around 140 million ECU/week (about $170 million/week).

The EC is confronted with an urgent need to adjust its agricultural policy to:

(a) reduce over-production of food and stocks;

(b) avoid the disturbance of international agricultural markets;

(c) maintain income to individual farms;

(d) protect rural society, and the natural environment.

Four solutions have been considered within the CEC to reduce the agricultural surpluses as indicated on the next page.

(a) cut support prices

(b) impose quota-levels;

(c) impose "extensification" (lower production from a given area);

(d) promote alternative land use, providing financial incentives.

For example, a "set-aside" scheme has already been approved (Regulation CEE 797/85) entailing for the year 1990, 1 million ha (of which 358,000 ha in Italy). Contributions of 226.5 million ECU from 1990, and 360 million ECU from 1992, have been approved as partial financial support by EC.

Alongside this action, strong support should be given to promote the production of (a) raw materials for industrial use where there is a large net deficit in trade, (for example, timber - 130 million cubic metres a year; cotton - 2.3 million tonnes a year), and (b) biomass crops for energy.

Besides a reduction in the huge cost of supporting the CAP, several other benefits for the EC have been identified resulting from the exploitation of biomass for energy and industry.

Socio-economic benefits: 50-60 per cent of the final production cost of biomass energy is manpower cost. The production of about 500 tonnes (dry matter) of biomass per year will create a new job in the bio-energy sector. Thus it can be envisaged that more than 600,000 new jobs could be created in the Community within the bio-energy sector, as well as further jobs in related industries such as the production of compost and pulp from paper, electricity production, ethanol, and in service organisations.

Environmental benefits: forest fire control (about half million ha/year are destroyed in the EC); improved erosion control; dust absorption; no sulfur emission (20 million tonne/year in the EC); improved soil - hydrology control; CO_2 absorption. Trees begin to absorb CO_2 as soon as they are planted, so large scale forestation and high yield cropping could provide a breathing interval while other solutions to the greenhouse problem can be implemented. One 1,000 MW_e coal power station will emit +4,300,000 tonne/year of CO_2 throughout its 40 year life and will require a forest of about 280,000 ha to absorb such an amount. (Old forests do not absorb photosynthetic CO_2 active at all or in very modest quantity. C4 crops plantations (three-four times photosynthetically more efficient) can considerably reduce such areas by a factor of between 2 and 4 times.

Modern bio-energy technologies and bio-fuels are relatively benign from an environmental viewpoint and produce very little pollution if burned correctly.

7.2 Biomass in the EC

The present usage is divided almost equally between industry and energy :

1. Present utilization

for industrial products[1]	30	M.toe (120Mm³)
for energy[2]	20	M.toe

2. Residues potential

from agriculture	107	M.toe
from forestry	20	M.toe
from wood industry wastes	8	M.toe
from refuse derived fuels	25	M.toe
	160	M.toe

References: [1]Saarbrucken,1988; [2]Hall D O and Rosillo Calle F, 1990.

7.2.1 *Future potential from energy crops* For a preliminary evaluation of the EC biomass long-term potential, the following main factors must be taken into consideration:

a. The potential land which will become available for energy industry farming is increased by the changes in land utilisation to reduce surplus production of cereals, sugar, wine, milk, and beef. This is forecast to be approximately 20m ha by the year 2000. (Saarbrucken 1988, and G.Grassi 1989).

b. Biomass crops productivity (target value in the period 1995-2000).

	Tonnes (dry) per ha per yr
Annual C4 crops (on good/medium agricultural land)	35
SRF (on low quality agricultural land	12-15
SRF (on marginal land, e.g. *Robinia*)	8-10
Special crops (on semi-arid land, e.g. *Cynara*)	20

Note: SRF = short rotation forestry

The medium and long-term biomass potential from energy crops in the EC can be estimated at 400 million tonnes of dry biomass (i.e. 20 tonnes/ha from 20 million ha). If converted to fuel liquids, this corresponds to around 130 Mtoe. By comparison, the crude oil consumption in the EC in 1989 was 462 Mtoe.

The above preliminary figures, concerning the EC future of biomass potential are so significant that a comprehensive assessment is important.

The Commission DG XII, has so far been able to identify promising new crops, and advanced technologies, for liquid fuels and electricity production through the implementation of its biomass programme (which started in 1975) and by rapid progress made in the last few years from other research programmes.

Adoption of new biomass resources (C4 crops: such as sweet sorghum, miscanthus etc.), of advanced technologies (flash-pyrolysis, up-grading process, aero-engine derived gas turbine generators, new process for pulp for paper production), and the integration of technologies with activities (bio-crude-oil, bio-ethanol, electricity, pulp for paper, compost etc) seem able to open new markets to the EC (without subsidies), which will never be saturated. Once inside never out. The new challenge for biomass production will be productivity per ha rather than the quality of the resources. Environmental constraints must of course be carefully assessed. The exploitation of this large potential will require a strong and imaginative effort for the conception, development, and definition of:

(a) an environmental framework for the production of biomass resources, distribution and rotation of crops)

(b) a technological framework (geographical, temporal, and the capacity distribution of the conversion and utilization plants)

(c) a social framework (temporal, geographical, and professional distribution of personnel).

7.3 Assistance to Developing Countries

The European biomass activity will also make a significant contribution to the solution of many serious problems of developing countries. The possibilities for conversion of biomass into liquid fuels and electricity will make it possible to supply part of the increasing demand for primary energy with local resources, and thus reduce demand for crude petroleum. Hence, bioenergy will play an increasing role in future cooperation schemes between Europe and the developing countries.

8. Summary and recommendations

This publication shows that the production of electricity from biomass, is a feasible way of making important contributions to the solution of several difficult problems facing the European Communities, and other countries too. It can:

(a) provide electricity at a cost comparable with the true cost of power from coal, oil or nuclear fuels, if due account is taken of the costs of pollution, disposal of wastes and de-commissioning of plant, and of socio-economic factors;

(b) offer a new market to agricultural producers;

(c) give new opportunities for rural employment and development;

(d) make significant contributions to the improvement of global and local environments.

The successful growth of a European industry producing power from biomass depends upon the identification, development and application of several diverse technologies at a pace that will allow the optimisation of the various interlocking parts, and the coordination of those parts into a coherent whole. The following steps are readily identifiable:

(a) Select the most productive plant species, taking into account regional variations in climate and soils.

(b) Determine the optimum conditions of growth, and the most economic methods of harvesting, preliminary processing, transport and storage.

(c) Develop appropriate technologies for the conversion of the raw biomass into solid, liquid and/or gaseous fuels including, where necessary, upgrading processes.

(d) Choose efficient engines that:

    i. are available at a size that is compatible with power demands
    ii. will run on bio-fuels efficiently and produce acceptable emissions
    iii. can be located as close as is practicable to the fuel source;
    iv. have low capital and running costs.

It will also be essential to ensure that institutional obstacles (such as tariff barriers or differential taxation) do not obstruct the development of power from biomass.

Further research is required to:

(a) develop pyrolysis and upgrading technologies for bio-oil;

(b) produce specifications for bio-oil to enable producers and users to trade in a reliable commodity,

(c) ensure that appropriate standards are set, and met, for emissions from gas turbines run on bio-oil or other bio-fuels,

(d) check that undue problems do not arise at any of the interfaces between the production of the biomass, its conversion into a fuel, and the exploitation of that fuel in the production of electricity.

The aim of this research is to establish, as soon as possible, a system of power from biomass, integrating advanced technologies from: agriculture, chemical engineering, design, manufacture and operation of engines, and electricity production.

9. References and bibliography

ALEXANDER A G (1985) The energy cane alternative, Elsevier, Amsterdam.

ANTONELLI L (1988) In: (eds) Grassi G, Pirrwitz D and Zibetta H Elevier Applied Science.

BAKER E G and ELLIOTT D C (1988) In: (eds) Bridgwater A V and Kuester J L, Research in thermochemical biomass conversion. Elsevier. p 883.

BAKER E G and ELLIOTT D C (1988) Catalytic upgrading of biomass pyrolysis oils. In (eds) Bridgwater A V and Kuester J L research in thermochemical biomass conversion. pp 883 - 895. Elsevier Applied Science.

BECKMAN D, ELLIOTT D C, GEVERT B, HORNELL C, KJELLSTROM B, OSTMAN A, SOLANTAUSTA Y and TULENHEIMO V (1990). Techno-economic assessment of selected biomass liquefaction processes. Final report of IEA cooperative project on direct biomass liquefaction. Report 697. Technical Research Centre of Finland: Espoo, Finland.

BEENACKERS A A C M and VAN SWAAIJ W P M (1986) Advanced gasification. Reidel, Dordrecht.

BRIDGWATER A V (1983) The contribution of thermochemical biomass conversion to the green-house effect. CEC internal documents.

BRIDGWATER A V (1991a) Costs of biomass pyrolysis derived fuels. In: (eds) Hogan E, Bridgwater A V, Robert J and Grassi G Proc. 1st CEC/Canada Joint Contractors meeting. Ottawa Canada. 23 to 25 October, 1990,

BRIDGWATER A V (1991b) Review of thermochemical biomass conversion. ETSU Report. UK Department of Energy.

BRIDGWATER A V and BRIDGE (1991) Review of biomass pyrolysis processes. In (eds) Bridgwater A V and Grassi G Biomass pyrolysis liquids upgrading and utilisation. Elsevier. pp 11 - 92.

BRIDGWATER A V and DOUBLE J M (1991) Technical and economic modelling of processes for liquid fuel production in Europe. Final report of CEC contract EN3V-0012.

CHANG C D, LANG W H and SILVESTRI A J (1976) US Patent 3 998 898

CHAVOT R (1990) Air gasification of biomass for the production of low BTU gas, CEC. Luxembourg (1990) Eur. Report 12678 EN, Cat. No. CD-NA 12678-EN-C.

CHEMISTRY AND INDUSTRY. (1990) Diesel nouveau? 5th November.

CHEN D E, WALSH D E and KOENING L R (1987) Amer. Chem. Soc., Div. Petr. Chem. Prepts. Vol.32. No. 2. p 264.

CHURIN E, GRANGE P and DELMON P EEC Contract EN3B-0097-B.

COOMBS J, HALL D O and CHARTIER P (1983) Plants as solar collectors: Optimizing productivity for energy, an assessment study. D Reidel Publishing Company, Dordrecht.

CORMAN J C (1986) System analysis of simplified IGCC plants. General Electric Company. New York.

DIEBOLD J and POWER A (1988) In: (eds) Bridgwater A V and Kuester, J L. Research in thermochemical and biomass conversion. Elsevier. p 609.

DIEBOLD J and SCAHILL J (1987) Amer. Chem. Soc., Div. Petr. Chem. Prepts. Vol.32, No.2 p 297.

ELLIOTT D C and BAKER E G (1987) In (ed) Klass D L Energy from Biomass and Wastes X. IGT, Chicago. p 765.

ELLIOTT T P and BOOTH R (1991) Sustainable biomass energy. Selected Papers. Shell International Petroleum Company Ltd.

EVANS R J and MILNE T A (1987). Energy and Fuel. Vol.1. pp 123 - 137 and 311 - 319.

GEVERT B (1987) PhD Thesis, Chalmers University of Technology, Gothemburg, Sweden.

INTERNATIONAL FLAME FOUNDATION (1990) Final report to CEC Energy from biomass programme. September.

GRASSI G (1989) Bio energy industrial integrated projects in the EC

GRASSI G and BRIDGWATER A V (1990) European research in biomass energy. Proc. 25th IECEC. NV. USA. AIChE. August.

GROENEVELD M J (1983) Production of a tar free gas in an annular co-current moving bed gasifier. In: (eds) Kjellstrom B, Stassen H and Beenackers A A C M, Producer Gas 1982, The Beijer Institute, Stockholm. p 235.

HALES S (1727) Vegetable statics or an account of some statical experiments on the sap in vegetables, being an essay towards a natural history of vegetation of use to those who are curious in the culture and improvement of gardening. Also a specimen of an attempt to analyse the air, by a great variety of chemico statistical experiments, which were read at several meetings before the Royal Society, London. (Reference found in: A J J Van De Velde, Jan Pieter Mickelers en het steenkool gas, Mededeling Van De Koninklijke Vlaamse Academie van Wetenschappen, Letteren en Schone Kunsten van Belgie, Brussels (1948)).

HALL D O, MYNICK H E and WILLIAMS R H (1990) Carbon sequestration versus fossil fuel substitution. The Centre for Energy and Environmental Studies. New Jersey.

HALL D O and ROSILLO-CALLE F (1990) Biomass, Bioenergy and Agriculture in Europe. King's College/London. CEC document (raw materials recycling).

KURKELA E, STAHLBERG P, MOJTAHEDI W and NIEMINEN M (1989) In: (eds) Ferrero G L, Maniaties K, Buekens A and Bridgwater A V. Pyrolysis and Gasification, Elsevier Appl. Sci. London. pp 304 - 311.

MANURUNG R and BEENACKERS A A C M (1985) Gasification of rice husk in a small downdraft moving bed. In: (eds) Palz, W, Coombs, J and Hall, D O Energy from Biomass. Proc. 3rd EC Conf., Elsevier Appl. Sci. Publ. Barking, UK.

MARROW J E, COOMBS J, and LEES E W (1987) An assessment of bioethanol as a transport fuel in the UK. Energy Technology Support Unit, ETSU - 44, Her Majesty's Stationery Office.

MANURUNG R and BEENACKERS A A C M (1989) An open core rice husk gasifier for small scale application. Proc. of the Second Int. Producer Gas Conference, Bandung 1985, The Beijer Institute, Stockholm.

PATURAU J M (1989) By-products of the cane sugar industry, 3rd edition. Elsevier, Amsterdam.

PAYNE J H (1991) Cogeneration in the cane sugar industry, Elsevier, Amsterdam.

RENAUD M, GRANDMAISON J L, ROY C and KALAIGUINE S (1987). Amer. Chem. Soc., Div. Petr. Chem. Prepts. Vol.32, No.2 p 276.

SAARBRUCKEN (1988) Euroforum new energies. Usage du bois comme source d'energie (Contrat SVII - 7030 - ETD/89-3) March 1991.

SCAHILL J and DIEBOLD J (1988) Engineering aspects of upgrading pyrolysis oil using zeolites. In: (eds) BRIDGWATER A V and KUESTER J L Research in thermochemical biomass conversion. Elsevier. pp 927 to 940.

SOLAR ENERGY RESEARCH INSTITUTE (1990) The potential of renewable energy. US Department of Energy.

SOLTES E J, LIN S-K and SHEU Y-H E (1987) Amer. Chem. Soc., Div. Petr. Chem. Prepts. Vol.37, No.2 (1987) 229.

SPERLING D (1989) New transportation fuels. University of California.

STEIN INDUSTRIES. Final report to CEC on pressurized wood gasification plant in Clamecy. (to be published).

WRIGHT L L, GRAHAM R L, TURHOLLOW A F and ENGLISH B C (1991) Opportunities to mitigate carbon dioxide buildup using short-rotation woody crops. In: (eds) SAMPSON R N and HAIR D Forests and global warming. American Forestry Association. Washington D.C.

Index